THE RAPE OF I

MW00799216

THE RAPE OF INNOCENCE

FEMALE GENITAL MUTILATION
& CIRCUMCISION
IN THE USA

PATRICIA ROBINETT

NUNZIO PRESS
EUGENE, OREGON

Nunzio Press
PO Box 256, Eugene, OR 97440
Phone 541.484.0731
www.NunzioPress.com

Robinett, Patricia
The Rape of Innocence: Female genital mutilation & circumcision in the USA
ISBN 978-1-878411-11-2

Revised and expanded edition of *The Rape of Innocence, Female Genital Mutilation in the USA* (Published 2006 by Aesculapius Press)

Printed in the United States of America
by CreateSpace, an Amazon.com company

With special thanks to my friends who worked with me on this book: Ava, David, Deidra, James, Jan, Jess, Kathy, Marilyn, Nan, Norma, Phyllis, Richard, Tom, Wendy

THE HUMAN RIGHTS OF CHILDREN

They shall not hurt nor destroy
in all my holy mountain:
for the earth shall be full
of the Knowledge of the Lord,
as the waters cover the sea.

Isaiah 11:9

This book is dedicated to children and to adults who protect children's rights. Children cannot speak for themselves, they cannot protect themselves. Children need people like you and me to speak for them and to protect them. To do that is a duty and a joy.

When adults with compassionate hearts protect helpless children from adults with sharp knives, there will be far less need for rights groups of any kind.

Peaceful, happy, healthy, contented babies grow to be peaceful, happy, healthy, contented adults who have no need or desire to hurt or destroy anyone or anything. Future generations will be as natural as they were created, as innocent as sheep, as wise as serpents and as harmless as doves.

"SPEAK TO US OF CHILDREN"

Your children are not your children.
They are the sons and daughters of Life's longing for itself.
They come through you but not from you,
and though they are with you yet they belong not to you.

You may give them your love but not your thoughts,
for they have their own thoughts.
You may house their bodies but not their souls,
for their souls dwell in the house of tomorrow,
which you cannot visit, not even in your dreams.
You may strive to be like them,
but seek not to make them like you,
for life goes not backward nor tarries with yesterday.

You are the bows from which your children
as living arrows are sent forth.
The archer sees the mark upon the path of the infinite,
and He bends you with His might
that His arrows may go swift and far.
Let our bending in the archer's hand be for gladness;
fr even as He loves the arrow that flies,
so He loves also the bow that is stable.

Kahlil Gibran, *The Prophet,* 1923

DID YOU KNOW?

- The genital cutting of both girls and boys was introduced in the USA in the late 1800s when all disease was blamed on masturbation. Blue Cross Blue Shield insurance paid for clitoridectomies until 1977.

- Although female genital cutting (FGM) was outlawed in the USA in 1996, the cutting of babies' genitals persists:

  - Babies born with ambiguous genitalia or Congenital Adrenal Hyperplasia (CAH) whose clitorises are "too large" or penises are "too small" are cut to conform to a medical "standard".

  - Mothers who have vaginal hospital births are routinely cut from vaginal opening to anus (episiotomies).

  - A third of all babies born in hospitals are delivered by major abdominal surgery — cesarean sections.

  - The first cut for nearly all infants born in hospitals is precipitous umbilical cord cutting, depriving infants of essential oxygen and blood from the placenta.

  - Healthy male genitals are still cut, usually the first day or eighth day of life, covered by medicaid in most states and by private insurance in all states.

DEFINITIONS OF TERMS

circumcise : verb : 1 : cut off the foreskin 2 : cut off the clitoris and sometimes the labia

circumcision : noun : the action or practice of circumcising

clitoridectomy : excision of the clitoris; female circumcision

episiotomy : a surgical cut made at the opening of the vagina at childbirth

genital : adjective : of, relating to, or being a sexual organ

innocence : noun : 1 a : freedom from guilt or sin through being unacquainted with evil : blamelessness b : chastity c : (1) : freedom from guile or cunning : simplicity (2) : lack of worldly experience or sophistication d : lack of knowledge 2 : one that is innocent

masturbation : stimulation of one's own genital organs

mutilation : noun : disfigurement, defacement, damage, injury, maiming, dismemberment, hurt

mutilate : verb : 1 : to cut up or alter radically so as to make imperfect 2 : to cut off or permanently destroy a limb or essential part of : maim, cripple, mutilate, batter, mangle mean to injure so severely as to cause lasting damage. *maim* implies the loss or injury of a bodily member through violence. *mutilate* implies the cutting off or removal of an essential part of a person or thing thereby impairing its completeness, beauty, or function.

rape : noun : 1 : an act or instance of robbing or despoiling or carrying away a person by force 2 : unlawful sexual activity and usually sexual intercourse carried out forcibly or under threat of injury against the will usually of a female or with a person who is beneath a certain age or incapable of valid consent 3 : an outrageous violation

sexual assault : noun : sexual contact that usually involves force upon a person without consent or is inflicted upon a person who is incapable of giving consent (as because of age or physical or mental incapacity) or who places the assailant (as a doctor) in a position of trust or authority

CONTENTS

The Human Rights of Children v

"Speak to Us of Children"...vi

Did You Know? vii

Definitions of Terms viii

My Story

Jesse Knew 1

A Child's Garden of Death 3

What Makes You Think It Would Be Any Different? 10

R-E-M-E-M-B-E-R ? 12

Telling a Little Girl's Story 14

A Daring New Adventure 18

They've All Been Traumatized 25

Circumcision 28

The Big Ugly 35

Why is a Girl Writing about Circumcision? 42

Circumcision Hurts Babies 45

There's Nothing There 51

Doctor, Do I Have A Clitoris? 59

All That's Left is a Scar 67

Examination by an Expert Witness 71

Your Mother Let Them Do That to You? 74

Where Did the Smile Go? 76

Society in Denial 80

Nothing is Irrational When All the Facts Are Known 86

My Family 92

Cut, Two, Three, Four 101

Sin & Punishment 105

They Really Got Me This Time, Kathy 113

A Happy Shift 118

Mother & Child Liberation 122

My Prayer 128

References & Resources

The FGM Bill 133

No National Medical Organization in the World 136

Reading & Viewing 139

For Reasons of Legality 148

MY STORY

JESSE KNEW

"Patricia, you're different from other women," said Jesse from the couch, peering thoughtfully over his reading glasses. What a dear man. He'd been watching me as I worked at the computer.

It was cold outside. The laundry was almost dry, and we were winding down for a long winter night.

Men had always said that. *You're different, Patricia — You're different from other women.*

I liked the idea of being different. I assumed they meant it in a good way. I never even thought to ask them *What do you mean, I'm different?... Can you say more about that?*

I assumed they meant I was more fun or more intelligent. But I never asked any of them. I would just smile and say *Thank you.*

And so again, I said, "Thank you, Jesse."

But Jesse was different from other men. He was more verbal, more perceptive and intuitive. He was more persistent, yet he was kind.

"No, Patricia, you don't understand. You're different from other women. Something happened to you."

"Like what, Jesse?" I asked, "What do you think might have happened?"

"Well, my ex-wife was sexually abused as a child and you remind me of her in a lot of ways."

"Oh, I don't think anything like that ever happened to me," I said. "I was a virgin until I was 18. I had no idea how sex worked until then."

"Well, all I know is that something terrible happened to you."

"Hmm. I really don't know what that could have been."

He seemed so sure.

Over the next few years a mystery began to unfold.

When the mystery was solved, I called my friend. *"You know what, Jesse? You were right! I am different from other women. Something awful did happen to me!"*

A CHILD'S GARDEN OF DEATH

Ten years before that conversation with Jesse, Mary Elizabeth Paddy Griggs Dixon Robinett Nickell, the woman who gave me birth, had driven all the way from Texas to Oregon with her second husband, my stepfather, to visit the house in the country where I lived with Tom.

Nick called to say that they were in the nearest tiny town, Marcola — just minutes away.

So I flew down the driveway bright in the sunlight, past the apple orchard fragrant in the clean summer air, and past the barn, to unlock the gate.

Here they come!

My heart was bursting. *Surely this time things will be different!*

The window on the passenger's side was open.

"Hi, Treesh!" said Mama with a smile.

Nick was driving. He grinned widely and said, "Get in!"

I opened the door and jumped in next to Mama. It was a tight squeeze and I had my arm around her shoulder. She laughed and nervously pulled away.

"I see you still have those knobby knees!" she laughed,

looking at Nick, away from me.

It was her way. Affection embarrassed her. And it was her way to say something derogatory about my appearance. She always did. Yet if you mentioned it, she would say *I was only teasing*. She'd say she liked to tease, that teasing was her way of expressing love.

The following morning, after a big breakfast, we all four leaned back in our chairs at the dining room table. Tom said something about how much he had enjoyed his childhood.

"Oh, not me." I said. "I hated being a child."

Whoops! Oops! Stone silence for an eternal moment. I knew I was in trouble when Mama sighed loudly.

Then she smiled sweetly, first to Nick on her right, then to Tom on her left, enlisting their support. Her gaze returned to me. Lifting herself up and forward with the palms of her hands flat on the table, she tilted her head to one side.

"But you were always such a happy little girl," she said.

Oh my! Here we were, prepared to battle, but this time other people were in the room. We'd never fought in public before. It had been our little secret.

Pushing my chair as far away as I could from the table, I said, "I was a *miserable* child."

Mom clucked her tongue as if to dismiss the idea. So familiar, that clucking sound! It reminded me of all the many times in my childhood when she had said, *That didn't hurt!,* correcting my perceptions and denying my feelings.

I always cried when reading or watching Thorton Wilder's play *Our Town*, about a woman who had died in childbirth but who then returned to visit the living. *All human beings are,* the character Emily said sadly, *blind people.* Indeed. All the years I'd lived with Mama, I'd felt unseen. Unheard. Untouched. Apart. Alone. Invisible. I felt that distance again.

But this time there were witnesses. Nick crossed his arms tightly over his big barrel of a chest. He saw a storm a'brewing. He had often asked why I didn't call much or come visit. Now he would know.

But then I realized — Mama honestly might not have known how extremely unhappy I had been. She may have never known. In one way, she was right: I had been a happy little child, a joyous little child — most of the time — when playing by myself, when Daddy was home, when others were around — for my first six years. But I wasn't usually happy when she and I were alone together and hardly ever after age six or seven. At that point something had broken but I couldn't quite remember what it was, how it happened or when.

I had only a few memories of my childhood.

I remember literally having been raised on a short rope. Mama used a harness to restrain me. *Children should be seen and not heard* was one of her favorite sayings.

She punished me for talking, so I didn't dare talk. She punished me for laughing, so I didn't dare laugh. She punished me for crying, so I didn't dare cry. My job description was to entertain myself quietly in my room or quietly outside in the yard — either way, I was to be quiet. I was not to be too happy, too noisy, too sad, or angry ever.

What remains when you take all those things away? Deadness and depression.

Thoreau wrote: *The mass of men lead lives of quiet desperation.*

So do the mass of children who are required to be quiet, always, everywhere.

Mama was drowning in her own private misery in those days. I remember her saying quite often *I wish I was dead* and *I wish you'd never been born.*

What's a child to do with proclamations like that? I took them on as if they were my own. I wept even in my mid-twenties over a particularly hurtful exchange...

So small that I had to stand on a chair at the sink to wash the dishes, the water cold and greasy, Mama's best crystal bowl slipped out of my hands and crashed into millions of pieces as it hit the floor.

"I'm sorry!" I said, ducking her blows. "It was a mistake!"

"So were you!" she snapped.

It was decades before I came to realize that many of my most negative thoughts and worst feelings were not my own. And so, at age 35, I finally began to give them back.

Thank you, but no thank you, I would say silently in my heart. *This is yours, not mine. I don't want it or need it, so I'm giving it back to you.* One thought at a time, recognizing the source and divorcing it, my emotional autonomy gradually returned.

I clearly remember in my late teens, watching a young mother kneel down to talk face-to-face with her four-year-old daughter. The little girl talked and the mother listened. The mother talked and the little girl listened.

I was astonished. For the first time in my life, I witnessed an intelligent and compassionate exchange between a mother and child. The woman treated her daughter as a person in her own right, as someone who deserved to be heard.

That scene was more amazing to me than a man walking on the moon. I learned a simple lesson that day. I learned that attention equals love... and some mothers give their daughters loving, respectful attention.

Mama's attitude, *What could children say that could possibly interest adults?* made me seriously doubt when she said, "I love you."

My brother, Mike, was devoted to Mama. He and his family often drove hours to visit her. But as far as I knew, Mama and Mike never talked much either. Mike was terse. If Mama asked him something, he would answer with one of two words: *Yes* or *No*. If she made a statement he would intonate, *Um hmm,* or utter a few sparse words... usually about sports.

Mike was tense. The muscles in his neck were locked tight. There might have been a lot of unspoken words sitting inside his throat.

Mike, his wife and children, Mama and Nick would watch television together — baseball, basketball, football or golf — then they would go out to eat, come back home, watch more TV, go to sleep and do it all over again the next day. After the weekend, Mike and his family would drive back home.

Nick had once said that when Mama crossed her arms over her chest, it would take days for him to pry unspoken fears out of her. Typically, she would joke, chit chat and complain, but was careful to never voluntarily reveal important thoughts and feelings. I inherited that tendency too. It took me many years to unlearn it. *Thank you, but no thank you.*

When we lived together all those years ago, Mama and I never sat chatting over a cup of tea, as she did with her friends.

Nobody in our family talked much at all. I thought of our house as a *cold war zone.* She and I had known each other more than four decades at the time of the conversation with Tom and Nick at the breakfast table in the dining room in the house in the country, but we still didn't know each other at all. Now at last we shared some time and tea and had a grown-up talk.

Everything I knew about communication I had learned from her, so it was possible Mama did not know how unhappy I had been. She honestly hadn't known.

We sat looking at each other in a dense cloud of silence. Did I dare talk about *it* now? Might as well — things couldn't get much worse.

This was one of my few clear memories of childhood. It was still as fresh at age 42 as it was when it happened and the words came tumbling out like a report, without emotion.

"When I was very young," I said, "I went to the kitchen in the middle of the night to get a knife to cut out my heart. But I was too little to reach the sharp knives. All I could find was a butter knife. And I knew that the rounded blade wouldn't work, so I went back to bed."

Silence. We four sat like stones around the breakfast table.

For once, Mama had no quick retort, didn't attempt to contradict me, reject or ridicule me. Miraculously, she actually seemed to have heard what I'd said. Everyone else at the table surely had. Simple, honest words go deep.

Suicidal ideation is what they call it when you have a plan and a clear picture of how to kill yourself. And I'd had a fine plan: I would lay on my bed and hold the knife straight up with the sharp tip of the blade between my ribs. It would hurt for a moment, but then I would pull hard and fast with both hands. I wouldn't feel anything as the knife pierced my heart. Once outside my body, I reasoned, I would fly free.

So we adults sat quietly contemplating the story of a child who had long ago wanted to kill herself.

I still could not and would not remember for many years, why it was that I had wanted to die but Mama offered one very important clue that same morning before our breakfast talk ended.

"You never were the same after your surgery" she said quietly.

"You mean my tonsillectomy?" I asked, for at that point I had no memory of any other surgeries.

"Y-yes," she stammered, looking down at her tightly clasped hands.

It would be fifteen more years, a few years after her death, before I would discover the nature of the surgery she referred to that day. But once I found out, brought it to conscious awareness and released the fear around it, my death wish dissolved.

WHAT MAKES YOU THINK
IT WOULD BE ANY DIFFERENT?

If any of the people — Mama or Nick or Tom — who sat at the dining room table in the country house had asked, *What happened then? After you went to the kitchen to find a knife and couldn't find one?,* I might have told them more. But as it was, since I had learned well that I couldn't trust anyone, I kept it to myself.

But I will tell *you* the end of the story.

Crawling back into my bed, I sighed in disappointment. I was looking forward to escaping this world.

But then something unexpected happened. During the quiet of the night, I heard a sweet, silent, safe, neutral voice. I remember to this day the tone, the cadence and the exact words: *What makes you think it would be any different if you were to die?*

Such a reasonable question, I thought. But it blew a hole in my reasoning. I had to admit that I didn't know for sure that I could leave my hell behind by killing my body. Now I was unsure whether I would actually achieve the goal of ridding myself of pain by killing my body. If the hell followed me beyond the body, I would have accomplished nothing.

I had never heard of reincarnation, but in this context I understood intuitively that if I opted out of the game at this point, I might have to repeat the painful years I'd already lived over again. This was a possibility that I *definitely* didn't want to risk. The thought of coming back and doing it all again was not an option.

From that time on, even though I never liked being on this planet, the question *What makes you think it would be any different if you were to die?* echoed in my mind. It followed me my entire life and those few words kept me from killing myself, no matter how bad things got.

REMEMBER?

In the same house in the country where Mama and Nick and Tom and I had our talk, I also had two of the scariest dreams of my life. This is one of them.

> *I wake up in the night and walk down the hall to the bathroom. The air is crisp and cool. The soft rays of the moon light up the room.*
>
> *I stop at the door and hesitate before I go in… Something is wrong. Very wrong.*
>
> *I always leave the shower curtain bunched up at one end of the tub, to allow the air to circulate and dry the tub, walls and fixtures. Now the curtain is spread across the tub from one side to the other, as if to hide…*
>
> *I hold my breath. Someone may be standing behind the curtain.*
>
> *On the side of the tub are big, bold, clumsy letters, written in bright red — lipstick or blood? I strain to read them…*

D I S M E M B E R

> *Dismember? Cut apart?*
> *The shower curtain rustles.*
> *I scream with all my might.*

In real life, I also screamed with all my might and sat straight up in bed.

"Tom?" I asked.

"Yes?" he said, sleepily.

"What do you think it did to your mind when they circumcised you?"

TELLING A LITTLE GIRL'S STORY

I am writing this book with the little girl I was before age six sitting quietly in my heart, in the green, green grass of my past.

She holds a stem of small white flowers that look like silver bells on a stalk.

What kind of flower is that, sweetheart? I ask.

A pretty flower, she smiles.

She brings the flower stalk to her nose so she can smell the lovely scent that is both dizzyingly sweet and hauntingly bitter. Then she lifts it up for me to smell too. She looks at me with trusting eyes.

She has been waiting patiently for several years now; waiting for me to tell her story. It is I who have hesitated. Telling her story has finally become more important to me than my fear. She has kept me moving, however slow my pace, by whispering often *Circumcision hurts babies.*

And although I intend to relate her story faithfully, fairly, kindly, lovingly, please forgive me if I fall short for I am only human.

The little girl in my heart knows that adults are rarely honest with themselves or others. She has seen them tell jokes to hide their embarrassment, cover their faces with handkerchiefs and pretend their sobs are coughs, put on brave faces — and all the while they are hurting, hurting, hurting inside: terrified of war, money, other people, judgment, God, germs, death — and even life itself. But especially they fear their darkest memories.

She knows that since I am an adult, I too am afraid to remember why it is I have always been so furiously angry and terribly sad. Instead of saying, *I'm having a bad day,* we adults will sometimes lash out at someone safe, like a child or a pet or someone we are certain will forgive us.

We clench our fists and grit our teeth and lie, *Fine! I'm fine!* when we feel like crying.

We boom, *This is the way it is, kid!* when we should say, *I don't know, sweetheart, I really don't know.*

We adults are far, far too busy busying ourselves and trying to act important, to simply be where we are, here and now, in the moment… in the green grass growing and cool wind blowing the white clouds moving through an endless blue sky touching our faces, breathing us, filling us up and emptying us out.

When others get too close, instead of being present and pleasant, we put on a vacant, distant, faraway, grown-up face with wrinkles in our foreheads, thinking, thinking, thinking, scanning back and forth, forth and back, here to the past and there to the future. Talking nonsense.

We ruminate on guilt, regret, fear, anger and resentment. That ruminating is our ruination.

Many of us are tense even when we are alone; always doing something. Though we may not say much, our minds are rarely quiet. We reach for food, alcohol, drugs, sex, music, television.

We work hard to fill the endless emptiness. All the while, deep inside, something in us is already peaceful and calm, powerful, confident and content.

Children think grown-ups are silly people. Many children say, *I'm never going to grow up!* because they don't want to grow up and be unhappy like the adults they see around them. The little lost children in Never-Never-Land sing, *I'll never grow up, never grow up! Not me! Not me! No, sir! Not me!*

The little girl inside me wonders, *Why don't adults listen to children? Love is attention. Adults should give children lots of attention. The world would be such a happy place if adults would only listen to themselves, to children and to one another.*

The little girl inside my heart wants our book to be a blessing for everyone — children and adults. She wants everyone to feel good about themselves and the decisions they make, especially decisions that affect children. She doesn't want anyone to hurt themselves or anyone else, ever. Especially she doesn't want them to hurt children.

She wants those of us who have made mistakes (which includes all of us) to put our mistakes in the past and to learn from them. We need to forgive ourselves and others because our unconscious guilt compels us to repeat mistakes. As Carl Jung wrote,

> *Until you make the unconscious conscious,*
> *it will direct your life and you will call it fate.*

Everyone has always done the very best they could under the circumstances, she says kindly. *It's good enough to say I'm sorry; I wish I hadn't hurt you in that way... Please forgive me... I won't do it again.*

The little girl inside me trusts my honorable intentions but she has also seen that I can be a wee bit of a verbal clumsy oaf once in a while. And that is why she is overseeing this very important project.

Cutting flesh hurts, she says, *but words cut too. Words can cut as deeply as knives. Please be kind.*

And so I try. Please forgive me if I forget at times that kindness is more important than being right.

A DARING NEW ADVENTURE

After that conversation at the dining room table in the country, things changed — *and fast!*

As Mama and Tom privately conferred in a corner about my fatal flaws (loudly enough for me to hear), it occurred to me that "Tommy" sounded a little too much like "Mommy".

So after Mom and Nick returned to Texas, Tom and I had our own first *real* talk. We cried together on the sofa, then we each left the house in the country.

Tom's parents were growing old and one of his sisters had cystic fibrosis, so he moved back to Denver to spend some precious time with his family. I moved into town where I shared a house with a businesswoman, her son, and a foreign student from the university.

Once settled, I turned all my attention to healing the mysterious feelings that made we wish to be dead. I was determined to have a happy life at last. My days and nights and all my waking hours were consumed with books, prayer and meditation.

I attended classes where students were taught to counsel one another and I took them more seriously than any I'd taken in college. I traded as much time as possible with my fellow students. Once I learned about the positive purpose of tears, I enlisted the help of my trusty, tame, pure white, unconditionally loving teddy bear to grieve my father's death from several years earlier...

One Friday evening I'd came home from my job in downtown San Francisco to find a short message on the answering machine. Since my brother Mike had never called me before, I suspected bad news. I dialed his number. There was no answer.

My friend Art arrived to take me out for the evening, and before we left, the phone rang. But it wasn't Mike — it was Mama.

"Puh.TREE.shuh?" Her tense, high-pitched English tone told me to, *Steel yourself! — Watch out!*

"Patricia," she continued, in a tone somewhat formal and military, "your father passed on."

His death had been sudden. He had a heart attack, went to the hospital and was gone within a day or two.

Poor Trudy, I thought. *She adored him and would miss him... as would my brother. I barely knew Daddy now.* It had been so long since I'd even seen him. I was rather numb.

I put the black handset back in its cradle.

"Do you want to stay home?" asked Art, kindly.

"No. Let's go to the party," I said. I didn't want think or feel. And I still had not, many years later, thought about or felt the loss.

So now it was years later, I was half a continent away, and I was ready at last to let go of the natural sorrow I had denied. My sweet-faced, unconditionally loving, non-judgmental teddy bear was my counselor for a day.

Teddy bear, I said softly, *Teddy bear, my Daddy died… Teddy bear, my Daddy died…* It took several repetitions, but soon a few warm, wet tears came to my eyes, melting years of frozen emotion.

Tears eventually flowed even more freely when someone told me I'd always been pure and innocent. Oh, how I had longed to hear kind words like those when I was a child!

One day, not long after, a thick and heavy book jumped off the bookshelf and landed in my hungry hands. It fell open and I read, *All healing is essentially the release from fear.* I was hooked — stunned by the simplicity! *Healing is always certain,* it said. *You are the holy Son of God Himself.* And then, something I'd never heard before: *God's will for you is perfect happiness.*

Much better, thought I, *than suffering.*

I wanted it! I wanted what that book was talking about. If I could have gained health, healing and happiness by eating its pages, I would have! The next time I opened the local weekly newspaper, I saw a tiny ad for a Sunday evening study group that focused on that very book! That study group has nourished me now for more than twenty years.

Then I heard from a friend that I could trade volunteer time for college-level counseling and crisis counseling classes at the local frozen-in-the-1960s social service organization. Eager to learn all I could about healing, I was thrilled!

White Bird was a surreal environment where bearded staff members with Ph.D.s wore tie-dyed or plaid flannel shirts and were paid minimum wage — including the CEO. His hallmark was twirling and twisting one greasy strand of hair down over his forehead. Yet he was a nonprofit Superman when it came to negotiating funding for White Bird programs with the local hospital, the university and law enforcement agencies.

White Bird was always as amazing and amusing as any television show or movie. It was *Mash* without the blood.

My specialty? Suicide, of course. I was dedicated to pulling clients out of self-destruct mode. If a client was suicidal, I would stay with them until they were free of their death urge, no matter how long it took. I loved the crisis department — I was in my element. Crisis and trauma were somehow familiar and comfortable.

Some folks on the staff at White Bird needed frequent cigarette and French fry breaks, and they could get mighty cranky after an hour. But something inside wouldn't let me leave the room until the client's fever had broken, no matter how long it took. The healing process doesn't punch a time clock.

After one lengthy session with a suicidal female client, she asked to see me alone. That was not usual White Bird protocol. We always worked in teams. The other counselor asked me how I felt about the idea and although I told him I felt safe, he waited outside the door.

When the client and I were alone, she took a small packet from the pocket of her jeans. "I want you to have these," she said.

She unfolded the paper to reveal four razor blades she had used to cut on her wrists. Her unspoken promise was clear. *I will never hurt myself again.* I carried those razor blades like precious gems to my waiting partner and together we safely discarded them.

I learned at White Bird that some things can be studied

in school: theory, diagnosis, technique, how to manage a business, etc. But healing doesn't always come from books. Healing comes from love. And love doesn't necessarily come on demand. Love comes in its own time. It has its own schedule. When we finally feel safe enough to let go of our fears and weapons of self-destruction, when we relax and let the breathe in again, then the healing comes. Love always shows up when invited. Shift happens and we can breathe again.

It became clear that I needed more time with clients than White Bird comfortably allowed. We were required to attach a mental disorder to each client. I began to understand that diagnoses did not always serve, as labeling clients only made them more fearful.

I stopped donating my time at White Bird when a client told me her sad material-world woes and I recognized that my own financial situation was far more dire than hers. Then another client needed to hear something beyond the White Bird philosophy, and I felt stifled. It was time to move on.

I rented an office. Appreciating my success with suicide cases, some White Bird supervisors sent me paying clients who didn't qualify for free treatment at the clinic. I put ads in the newspaper to announce my new adventure.

I loved my clients and I loved my work. There came a point when it didn't matter who was sitting in the white leather recliner in my office — they were my very favorite person in the world — until the next person came in and sat down in that chair — and then they became my very favorite person in the entire world. I knew then that I had succeeded in reclaiming a large part of my long-lost heart.

Thanks to my clients, I learned how the horrendous impact of unhealed trauma plays and replays, year after year, lifetime after lifetime; how it pushes our shoulders down and punches our stomachs in, sits on our chests and sucks us under until we can barely breathe. I learned the advantages of releasing fear as quickly as possible.

I saw clients unconsciously, compulsively reliving the past, rerunning uncomfortable, unresolved stories that were sometimes eons old. When they finally felt safe in the present moment, here and now and released fear from the past, they quickly, easily moved on. It was my job to get them there.

One of two things happened when someone released the fear. Either the pattern broke and they never had to experience the same condition again — or if it did occur, there was no longer a *charge* in it for them. Either way, they were free.

I was my own most diligent client. And every client was my healer. Healing is never a one-way street; true healing is always an equal exchange.

With my clients as teachers, I gained a deep sense of appreciation for self-honesty. It takes courage to acknowledge feelings that — like lonely, neglected and abused children — call for our attention. Together my clients and I would look at uncomfortable feelings. We listened carefully and respectfully to the stories those feelings wanted to tell, until the fever broke.

As much as my clients benefitted, I also benefitted. As I talked them into a state of deep relaxation, one by one the tensions in my own body disappeared. My body relaxed and after a long history of ill health I became strong, energetic and pain-free.

My world view became less judgmental. I saw that there are no good guys, there are no bad guys; *there is only fear and love.* And we are always doing the very best we can.

When we feel love, we are naturally kind and generous. But when we feel frightened, we get out the big guns — *to ostensibly defend ourselves!* — and sometimes we shoot ourselves in the process. We push good, kind, loving people away, scare friends off, rejecting them first, fearing that they will reject us.

I learned that someone who acts tough and threatening is usually the one who is the most frightened, the most hurt. If you check beneath the surface, you find that anyone who harms another is himself reeling from unhealed, unresolved traumas. He staggers around, disoriented, unconscious, unaware. Lashing out in rage and fury, he doesn't realize he hurts himself as much or more than anyone else. The most abusive people are running from their own pain. The most fearful put on the scariest face. *The best defense is a good offense.*

Anger is fear. Violence is fear. Sorrow is fear. And for every form of fear, the appropriate response is compassion. All fear-based behavior is a call for love and healing.

When we turn on the lights and look at the phantoms of the past, we inevitably discover that the ghosts were only cob-webs. Ultimately, we find there is nothing to fear, *even death, for we do not die.* Knowledge is freedom.

I sensed that I was working as a healer so I could learn more about healing and ultimately heal myself. At this time, I still had no idea what the unhealed trauma was that ran my personal relationships. So I continued to gather information, to grow in understanding, and to prepare myself.

THEY'VE ALL BEEN TRAUMATIZED

Gary was a research psychologist who specialized in *Post Traumatic Stress Disorder* (PTSD). We sometimes talked for hours on the phone about his work, my research into circumcision — and his interest in a beautiful, unattainable woman.

Even though she had a boyfriend and was not at all interested in Gary, he spent an inordinate amount of time thinking about her, talking about her and longing for her. Other women wanted to date him, but he didn't want *those* women. He only wanted the one he *couldn't* have.

Why are men like that, I wondered one afternoon after we'd said goodbye. *Why do men want women who don't want them? Why do men shun women who do want them? Why do men like women who ignore them and who treat them poorly? Why do they resent the ones who treat them well?*

And from there my wondering grew. *Why are men reluctant to be friends with women? Why do they seem to be uncomfortable with affection unless it involves sex? Why are they so easily manipulated by sex? Why do men turn the most innocuous, neutral, innocent thing, like a carrot, into a sexual innuendo? Why all the pornography?*

In 2001, Dan Ackman in *Forbes Magazine* estimated porn to be a $2.6-3.9 billion business while Frank Rich in the *New York Times Magazine* said $10-14 billion. Either way, it's big business. Yet few women are addicted to porn, so most of that money comes from wallets, not purses. Pornography fortunes are fueled primarily by men's money. *Why?* Is it due to the missing skin? Does porn fill a need that their bodies are not filling due to sense deprivation?

And then there's danger and violence. *Why all the competition, fast driving, drinking, smoking and drugs? Why do men, far more often than women, pick fights at bars, wage wars with other countries, break the law? Why do they like loud noises and combative, predatory, violent sports like boxing, wrestling, football, and hunting? Why do four times the number of men commit suicide as women?* One huge, unanswered question loomed: *Why are men the way they are?*

Some say it's the testosterone. Some say it's because of women. But no, males in Europe are not all that different from females say Richards, Bernal, and Brackbill in their 1976 article "Early Behavioral Differences: Gender or Circumcision?" in Developmental Psychobiology.

There's something about American men. There has to be something more, I thought. *There has to be a deeper reason, a truer reason than anyone has come up with so far — something assumed, something taken for granted, something so obvious that I can't see it... yet.*

Most of the women I know appreciate men who are available. They bond with their men and stay with them. They are loyal, even when it's difficult. My female friends do not pick fights. They've not been suicidal as children.

Suicidal? The eye of the camera began to turn toward me. Zoomed in for a close-up. I began to see that many of the same traits I saw in men were mine as well.

I sought out mystery and romance. I preferred excitement to comfort and security. Like many men, I toyed with danger. I had always walked the cutting edge. I had a tendency to be self-destructive. After all, as a child I wanted to cut out my heart!

I both resented and yet understood men's fear of marriage, for I couldn't wrap my mind around it either. The prospect of spending my life in a house behind a white picket fence, with an adoring husband, smiling children, a cat and a dog and a Volvo in the garage scared me more than a den full of hungry lions and tigers.

My shoulders fell. I had no idea what to make of this.

OK! I give up! I need a miracle. Aloud I said, *I am willing to see men differently.*

What I heard then was a kind, neutral, silent voice… *They've all been traumatized.*

Yes, OK, I agreed, *childhood trauma can affect a person's entire life. But how were they traumatized? What kind of trauma?*

After a short pause, one more silent yet distinct word…

CIRCUMCISION

Circumcision?

An alarm rang in my mind: *Danger! Danger! Danger!*

Usually, I'd press the snooze button and ignore the wake-up call. I'm glad I didn't this time. This time the alarm was so loud I couldn't ignore it.

It was time for me to begin to remember what I had long ago forgotten. D I S M E M B E R , R E M E M B E R ?

The word *circumcision* had, for some reason, always lived a life of its own beneath my conscious radar. There must be something important for me there, in that word *circumcision*. But so far it was only a word. A word that was somehow tied to a world of confusion.

I began trying to put it all together. I realized that every time I had ever heard the word *circumcision,* it was as if a bell sounded — *Ding!* — I would sit up a little straighter and my mind would go blank.

Searching my files. *Yes! Here it is!* A well-worn file folder labeled "Circumcision". It was filled with papers. I couldn't remember when or where I had started that file. Texas? San Francisco? Denver?

And as if that wasn't enough, all forms of the word *circumcise* were highlighted in my *King James Bible* — and even though I surely had done the underlining, I couldn't remember when or where or why. If the word *circumcision* was in the Bible, did that make it "holy"? Did that mean it had something to do with "God"?

Despite signposts pointing to the fact that I must have given some thought to circumcision, I had to admit that I didn't know exactly what the word meant. So far, it was still an abstraction, a vague idea, a mystery. Yet something in me knew that the word was personally significant. I'd heard it in a context I could not consciously recall.

In my mind, the word blinked on and off — big capital letters and bright, bold, neon lights. *Danger! — Warning! — Watch out! — Block your heart!* But the reason for this colorful Las Vegas scene was fuzzy and in the background. An important memory had been lost long, long ago.

The one thing I was absolutely clear about was that circumcision was taboo. People don't talk about circumcision in Kansas. That much I knew.

From the Bible, I remembered that circumcision involved Jewish baby boys, Abraham and Isaac and a covenant. From *National Geographic*, I knew it involved African teens, had something to do with coming of age and something to do with penises.

My mind zoomed to the past, to everyone in my life who was Jewish. As far as I knew, there was not much diversity in the white Anglo-Saxon Protestant town where I grew up.

It wasn't until my senior year of high school that I was aware of Jewishness in any form. I really didn't know.

HIGH SCHOOL

Two brothers Marty and Larry, Marty's wife Ellen and their little girl and baby boy moved in across the street from my parents when I was a senior in high school. The brothers had moved from New York City to Kansas City to study medicine.

Marty explained that he didn't allow his children to use baby talk, like *pee* and *pooh* but instead taught them to use the proper adult words: *urinate* and *defecate*. That both impressed and embarrassed me. Across the street in our house we didn't use any of those words. Instead, we were taught to say, *I have to go to the bathroom.*

One day a package full of bagels and lox and cream cheese, shipped on dry ice arrived from Marty's parents in New York City. I was called across the street for a spontaneous party.

We munched our delicious treats and then watched a movie from the brothers' medical school — a hospital birth with bright red blood flying all over the room.

They joked and laughed throughout the movie, but as soon as it ended, I left in a state of shock.

Naive and virginal, I'd had no concept of what birth entailed before that day. I'd never given it much thought. I had no idea how babies were made. *There was so much blood!*

I had long ago made a decision not to have a family due to my mother's frequent, bitter curse: *I hope you have six children just like yourself!* The birthing movie firmed my resolve, adding to the curse a messy, bloody, dangerous, painful ordeal.

I don't remember my New York neighbors mentioning

what they did with babies after the birth. With a baby boy, surely they knew about circumcision. But they didn't talk about *that*.

COLLEGE

College, quite frankly, was even more of a blur. A girl in my scholarship hall was plain, blond and Jewish. She majored in history and grew up to be a famous mystery author. Everyone else in Kansas, as far as I knew then, was Lutheran or Catholic.

LOS ANGELES

After college, I met Annie in Los Angeles. She was great fun to be around — a lively, loving, assertive woman, a good friend to many. Annie, who was very short, was an honorary den mother for half a dozen big, beautiful, protective black men twice her size. She had a wonderful way of making sure everyone felt included and we were all happily entertained.

Annie's gynecologist diagnosed her with endometriosis and told her that the only way he knew for her to get rid of it was to have a baby. She wasted no time. She enlisted the help of one of her adoring male friends to help her do just that — *and it worked!*

She got pregnant, reversed the endometriosis, and had a beautiful half Jewish, half African-American son.

But no… she had never said anything to me about circumcision.

ROMANTIC PARTNERS

Two Jewish boyfriends. Nary a word from either on this most sensitive of subjects.

AT WORK

The first wisp of a conversation I remember ever having about circumcision was only ten years ago when my Jewish boss asked if I understood all the words in the ethnic jokes his Jewish friends had sent him by e-mail.

"Most of them," I said, "but what is a *bris*? I don't know why, 'Never accept a front row seat at a *bris*' should be funny."

"That's the ceremony where they circumcise the baby," he said succinctly.

Ding! He'd said the magic word. I sat up straight. My mind went blank.

He went back to his office. Not another word was spoken at that time on that subject. Now I knew a little more, that a *bris* is a circumcision ceremony but I didn't dare ask him what they did to the baby. Perhaps he assumed that I knew what circumcision was, what they did at a *bris,* and therefore why I should not take a front seat. He overestimated me.

BACK TO THE PRESENT

Back to the moment after I heard, *They've all been trauma-tized… circumcision.* Naturally, I wanted to know more…

- What exactly *is* circumcision?
- What exactly *do* they do to the baby?
- Why exactly should I *not* take a front row seat at a *bris*?
- Why *are* so many men the way they are if circumcision is only a religious thing for a rather small percentage of the population? For it wasn't only the Jewish men who mystified me — it was Christian men too.

So many questions in my mind.

WHY HAD I NEVER HEARD ABOUT CIRCUMCISION?

Perhaps I was the only one in the world who did not know what circumcision was. In my *speak-no-evil* home and straight-laced Kansas high school, sex education was virtually non-existent. As far as I knew, people in Kansas did not have genitals. They certainly never talked about them. Words like *phallus* or vagina never crossed our minds, let alone our lips.

We did have a brief *sex-education-lite* class one day for one hour in the auditorium of the high school. What did they teach us? They taught us a word: *menstruation.* And they taught us how to use an elastic G-string-type contraption that held a *sanitary napkin* against our bodies to collect the bloody discharge, which was then to be discretely discarded in a box labeled, *sanitary napkins.*

Shortly after this class, which was surely sponsored by the company that made sanitary napkins, Mama nervously asked me to come outside for our first and last walk in the backyard. Her voice shook and her eyes were on the ground. "There's something I have to tell you," she said.

"It's all right," I said, for I suspected our talk was to be about sex and I was as embarrassed as she was. "They already told us in school."

Voila! A relief to us both! That was the beginning and the end of our first and last, one and only mother and daughter birds-and-bees talk.

Twenty years later, attending the University of Texas in Denton, I surely would have heard a lot of interesting information had I been in town when my wild and crazy, tenured University of Texas anatomy teacher lectured on human sexuality, but unfortunately (or perhaps fortunately), I was in Florida on that day.

That man taught us that *fangers* was Texan for *fingers,* so I wonder if he taught us that *paynis* was Texas for *penis.* He loved to shock his classes, so I suspect he talked about circumcision that day.

Circumcision. The word itself holds a few little clues. *Circum-,* as in *circumference* means *around* and *-cision,* as in *incision* means to *cut. To cut around.*

But cut around exactly what? A penis? And cut how around a penis and exactly where? And exactly why? I had a head full of hook-like question marks.

So I stepped over to my computer and slowly, deliberately typed the letters C I R C U M C I S I O N and hit the return key...

I was not at all prepared for what I saw next.

THE BIG UGLY

A tiny, screaming baby. Contorted face. Rigid body. A tender, vulnerable, newborn baby boy who had been curled up in a ball for nine months in the womb was stretched out flat on his back and strapped down spread-eagle. His penis was erect. There were clamps, a razor sharp scalpel. And there was plenty of raw skin and red blood. His penis was being skinned.

I turned away; closed my eyes. I had already seen more than enough blood for a lifetime when my neighbors showed the hospital birth movie. And now *this*?

The word *violence* comes from the French word *viol* (rape). To violate another is an act of violence, of rape.

This is so very violent. Raping babies. Knives and blood. Genitals and screaming. This is what they euphemistically call *circumcision*?

It was just a photo on a website — John Erickson's SexuallyMutilatedChild.org — but my whole life was there in that moment with that baby — heart racing, adrenalin pumping, every muscle tensing, fighting, squirming, struggling, screaming, crying, trying with all my might to get away from that knife. It shocked my mind. It broke my heart.

Aware of how deeply trauma imprinted minds, I saw a disaster in the making: an innocent consciousness thrown into fear and plunged into feelings of helplessness, hopelessness, powerlessness, loneliness, isolation, terror, panic, anger, sex, and violence. And not just one baby. Not just one religion. Almost all North American baby boys were circumcised in the 1970s and still more than half are cut in the USA when they are only a day old.

WHERE IS HE NOW?

I couldn't help but wonder, *Where is that poor baby now? What is his life like today?*

Did his mama love his fear away? Or did she leave him alone because he screamed and cried all the time? Did they call him "cranky"? Did he punch other children in kindergarten?

Is he happy and peaceful? Or has he lived his entire life kicking and screaming in reaction to this long-forgotten trauma?

Is he one of the men who imagines his two-tone penis was designed like that by nature? Does he avoid sex? Or pursue it like a rabid dog? Is he obsessed by his penis? Fixated on it? Does it require heroic measures for him to enjoy sex? Is he rough with his own body or his partner's?

Is he comfortable and relaxed in his body? Or is his body tense and his posture rigid?

Does he genuinely love and trust people? Or does he use and abuse them? Does he push them away? Does he run away? Does he hide away in alcohol, drugs or work? Does he then wonder why he is alone?

Does he scream aloud or silently inside, "Leave me alone! Don't touch me! Go away! I hate you!" Can he trust anyone?

Does he have a drive to manipulate and control circumstances and people? To keep himself safe, without regard to the welfare of others? Does he leave disaster in his wake? Does he think it's normal to be angry? Violent? Harsh? Timid?

In that photo I saw rape. If the victim had been an adult, a girl child — or even an animal — the man in the white coat would have been jailed.

If it wasn't so common here, newspapers would surely shout about it on the front page. Human rights organizations would be outraged. If people knew more about the practice, they would no longer use the sanitized word, *circumcision*. They would call it what it is — inhumane, rape, torture, sexual mutilation, assault and battery.

I wondered, *How can we be so oblivious to the harm this practice causes?*

Could it be because — like me — so few really know what circumcision really is?

Probably so. I hope this book will help.

MILLIONS UPON MILLIONS HAVE BEEN CUT

I read more. More than a *million* baby boys are circumcised *each year* in the United States — *one child every 26 seconds.*

No wonder, I sighed. *No wonder there are so many lonely, unhappy, desperate, confused, angry men.* It would be difficult to imagine a more insidious wound to the body and psyche — of an individual or of a culture — than the overpowering of a baby and the dismembering of his tender genital flesh. Physically restraining an infant, handling his private parts, cutting on them… the child fears for his life in that situation.

If our society could see genital cutting from a rational, objective perspective, it surely would consider circumcision as child abuse, torture and mutilation. But no. We clearly see what they do "over there" in other countries — primitive people in primitive countries — as wrong, bad and in need of rectification, so we feel justified in throwing stones at them. But are we without sin? Can we even see the plank in our own eye?

Overpower! Sex! Violence! Cutting! What are we doing to our young? What are we teaching them?

From my work with clients in hypnotic regression, I was, by this time, well aware how far-reaching trauma can be when it happens in infancy. Children are so much more aware and sensitive to pain than doctors once imagined. The wordless terror children feel when abused is welded to every cell. Extreme fear can affect their ability to breathe and feel safe for the rest of their lives. Why would anyone ever do harm to a baby?

Circumcision leaves both physical and psychological scars. I can only guess what the world would be like today if the United States hadn't been amputating the genital tissue from a majority of its male infants for the past 55 years.

Common sense says, *if we had been kinder to our babies, they might have grown up to be kinder, gentler, more compassionate adults. If they had not been terrified as babies, perhaps they would not feel such a need to police and control the world.*

The implications of this horror, intentionally inflicted by human hands on babies, instantly overshadowed nearly every other concern I had ever had about my life and the world in general.

Could this be the root of man's inhumanity to man?

No matter how cruel, every perpetrator has first been a help-less victim and here we are, manufacturing a potential perpetra-tor every time we circumcise an infant. Chances are, when he is a father, he will insist that his sons be circumcised... to look like him.

I shook my head and looked away from my computer, out into the trees beyond the window.

My! That was a long, deep journey in a very short space of time. A fast class of shocking facts.

Then I had a little conversation with myself.

This is it, Patricia. More than half the male population of the United States has been badly wounded. Circumcision is a big clue to the phenomenon of "man's inhumanity to man". This is your work, girl! Time to write a book.

Well then, thought I, *I need to know everything I can about this subject of circumcision.*

Turning back to my computer, I began to read... and read... and read... I joined an Internet mailing list for *intac-tivists,* people who are actively working to educate parents and doctors, legislators and the judiciary about circumcision.

There was so much information on the Internet that I could have read for hours and days and months and now I have read and researched for over ten years. I am still reading and learning. I feel the pain of those who regret their experiences involving circumcision. There are so many stories, such as:

> "My sister's first husband was cut when he was 13, by his own father and uncle, at home! He had to hear his big brother being cut first, then it was his turn..."

"I was traumatized at a young age by watching my baby brother, who had just been cut, scrape the bandages off his penis and scream and bleed all over his crib. At that point I think I decided my sons would not be cut."

A man came running up to my car once because he saw the bumper sticker that says, "Circumcision hurts babies". He wanted to tell me his story. He said that one afternoon when he was about 12 years old, he and the other boys in his school class were sent to the doctor's office.

He was led to a room, told to take his pants off, put on a gown, and sit on the table in the middle of the room. He did what he was told, but after a few minutes, the wheels in his head began to turn.

He put on his clothes, left the room, walked out of the doctor's office, and ran all the way home over hills and through meadows. for his family lived far outside of town. His mother was surprised to see him home so early.

She said, "You were supposed to go to the doctor's office."

He said, "No!" and that was the end of the discussion.

If we asked babies and children, that is surely what they would all say: "No!" But we don't ask. We trick and/or coerce, inflict our will on babies who are too young to speak up for themselves. That is why this book exists... to speak out for the babies who cannot speak for themselves.

One woman wrote to others who have become educated about circumcision in the USA:

> I sometimes wish I had just gone and thrown myself between my nephew and that doctor, even if it meant hospital security would have dragged me out.

If anyone else — friend or family — refuses to become educated on the subject when it is one I have spent the past 10 years studying and working with, and allows their perfect little newborn baby to be raped at the end of the knife, they are no longer someone I wish to associate with in any way. If a family member tied down and genitally mutilated an adult, it would be termed "sexual assault" and I would not stand by and quietly infer that it was okay to do. It is certainly not okay to do the same to a non-consenting, helpless baby, fresh and new to this earth.

When we don't speak up, we are just as guilty as those doing it. And when we don't say "This is wrong!" we imply that it is okay. I don't my children to grow up around those who believe it is alright to harm another human life just because someone feels like it (especially a baby who cannot defend himself).

It's time for open, honest communication and education, 100% transparency. It's time for us to scrutinize all our beliefs, including religious, medical and social practices, so that if there is an addiction of some sort to the sexual use and abuse of babies and children, it can at last be laid to rest.

Ending abuse is a gift to everyone. Allowing it to continue is abusive to both victim and abuser. Those who abuse hate themselves.

WHY IS A GIRL WRITING ABOUT CIRCUMCISION?

"CIR-cum-CIS-ion!?"

My friend John paced around the room and threw his arms about. He was agitated, animated, riled up. I'd never seen him like this.

"You? You're writing a book about *circumcision!? You're* a *girl!* You *can't* write a book about *circumcision! Girls* shouldn't write books about *circumcision!"*

John is usually a quiet, mild-mannered, more-peaceful-than-thou kind of guy. But he'd just read something I had written: *Circumcision Hurts Children.* He was the second man I'd shown this article to, and the second man to have turned green from reading it.

"I don't know, John. It just seems that it's what I'm supposed to do."

But John didn't appear to hear me. He just kept pacing and flailing, raising his eyebrows, and talking in a volume louder than usual.

"Guys should write about *circumcision! Circumcision* is a *guy* thing, *not a girl thing!* You should write a book about something

like.... like... like..." He stops and looks at me directly and throws his arms out again, "... like... *breast cancer!* Write about *breast cancer. Don't write about circumcision.* Let a *guy* write about *circumcision.*"

There was a long, awkward silence.

"I'm sorry, John, but breast cancer doesn't interest me at all. I'm not writing a book just to write a book. I'm writing about circumcision because it's an important topic. For some reason, it chose me. It's a juicy, meaty, sexy subject. And I'm writing about it — *even though I am a girl.*"

How could I tell John that writing about circumcision feels like some kind of an assignment from God? And how can I tell him that his upset *may be due to his own forgotten trauma? Might the article have restimulated his own unhealed distress?*

"John, baby boys are powerless against grown-ups. When they are strapped down and circumcised against their will, they can still carry feelings of powerlessness forty years later. Circumcision has been a source of trauma for most of the men in this country. They're so angry their words don't come out right, and even when they do say it right, everybody else gets upset.

"Men don't want to think that the most sensitive part of their penis was cut off and thrown in the trash. Parents don't want to think they might have allowed someone to hurt their children. Doctors and nurses don't want to think they've harmed helpless children. Some psychologists and psychiatrists can't even listen to men lament. They tell clients, *You're obsessing! Get over it!*

"Circumcision is a very difficult subject for people to think about, talk about, write about, read about.

"This book needs to be written by a woman. A woman can say things men can't. Men aren't supposed to complain, but a woman can complain about male circumcision. Women can protect their babies and their men.

"This subject *needs* a woman's voice."

"But *why?*" he persists. *"Why* are *you* writing a book about circumcision?"

Now I see what a very excellent question that was. I really didn't know yet why I in particular was writing a book about circumcision. Maybe because I thought I could write more objectively, since I was a girl and hadn't been circumcised.

Soon I would become aware of how appropriate it was that all this was unfolding as it was. It would be only a short time before I'd be able to provide an answer to his question.

Why is *a girl writing about circumcision?*

CIRCUMCISION HURTS CHILDREN

"Other people's surgery," they say, "is always minor surgery."

Many people have difficulty reading about circumcision or watching a video. If observation bothers adults, imagine how the act itself affects little children.

Circumcision hurts children — and the adults they become. This chapter is a reality check for those who maintain circumcision is "just a little snip." It takes circumcision out of the realm of denial. After all, if the same thing happened to an adult, wouldn't it be considered sexual assault, battery and mutilation?

If you were circumcised, imagine what going through such an experience did to you. Your anger, depression, anxiety or distrust now make more sense, don't they? They're not irrational. You are not irrational.

Now you know where to work — at the source, the core, the origin of this primal trauma. I have heard that injury caused intentionally by another human carries far more negative weight than injury stemming from other sources. Much healing is needed due to the circumcision assault.

Heal this fear, release this trauma, and you will be healthier than you could ever imagine. The key is to know that the insult happened in the past and that you are safe now.

> WARNING : This section contains mentally and emotionally disturbing images. Please do not read it when you are tired, hungry, cold or feeling vulnerable, sad, angry or anxious. Do not read it just before bed. You don't have to read it. You can skip over it and go to the next section. This is an optional part of the book.

Before we start, get comfortable. Close your eyes for a moment and take a breath. Tell yourself, *I am safe here and now.* Know that the past is in the past and you can look at the past as you would a movie.

Allow yourself to close your eyes whenever you start feeling any distress and remember to notice your breath. Notice that it is breathing you, moving you, soothing you and comforting you.

Let your shoulders and buttocks relax.

Sink into the chair or sofa or bed you are resting on. Make sure your head and neck are supported and begin to remember a time when you felt peaceful — very, very peaceful. Allow the burdens you've been carrying to fall from your shoulders, arms and hands. Let all of the tightness and tension melt out of your face and jaw. Read this with a gentle tone of voice.

Imagine... the incredibly delicious sensation of floating in a pool of warm, welcoming water.

Sleepy, happy, your eyes are comfortably closed. You are loose and limp. Every muscle is soft. Floating peacefully in warm water. Your body undulates gently to the pleasing rhythm. You are open. Acutely aware of your exquisitely sensuous body. Moving. Flowing. Floating. Sounds of soothing waves. Beautiful, muffled sounds of voices echoing through the thick water. Everything's soft here. No hard edges. Nothing harsh. Nothing sharp or rough. Everything is smooth, soft, warm, wet, wonderful.

Then a rhythm starts to build. This is new and different and a little bit shocking. It's getting a little tight in here. You are squeezed, twisted, turned upside down and you wiggle your way through a tunnel until you are finally pushed out and dumped into an uncomfortable, cold, endlessly cold, empty, dry, cold world.

Giant hands grab you. Bright lights burn your eyes. Loud sounds blast your ears. The cold air bites your skin.

The connection to your blood, oxygen and food supply is suddenly interrupted. Everything stops. Food. Blood. Oxygen. All stop. You panic. You feel so alone.

But, no! — You are not alone! The giant hands jerk you up into the air by your heels. They slap you. You gasp and strain. Cold, biting air, cold dry air pierces your lungs. You scream. They laugh.

"Great lungs! *It's a boy!*"

Like a cruel fraternity hazing, giant hands pass you around. They poke, pierce and prod your every orifice. They place you on cold metal that sears your skin like fire. Unspeakable odors and flavors, noises and lights overwhelm your every open, inquiring, acutely aware, curious nerve ending.

Finally they bind you, and lay you in a cage with bars. Such a hard bed. Exhausted, you sleep. You dream of floating.

You still remember floating.

When you awaken, your mother holds you and sings to you as she did before, when you were still together, before the storm. You are safe again! Warm, in her loving arms. Mother and baby, together at last.

Then — the others return. They take you from her. They make you naked. Exposed. They turn you this way and that. You are cold again, and dizzy.

No one helps you. Isolated. Where is mother?

You are now laid on a cold, rigid plastic board. You know something bad is going to happen. You want to curl up into a ball. You don't feel safe. You want to protect your soft, vulnerable parts.

You, who were curled in a nice soft ball forever in the womb, are now forced flat and strapped spread-eagle to the board. They pull your legs and arms farther apart than they have ever been stretched before. You are stretched and strained. It feels like you will break. You struggle to escape. Only your head can move.

What are they going to do to you?

Terror!

Cold hands reach between your legs. They grab your good-feeling part and rub it with a cold liquid. Interesting. Captivating. A five-minute scrub. All of your attention is now focused on your penis. Erection. A big person is doing something to the sexual part of a small person.

Then comes another giant hand. It holds your penis. It still feels good. But then a blunt instrument is jammed between the unripe shaft and its preputial covering.

No! No! Your mouth and eyes open wide in astonishment. Your entire body stiffens. You want out of here — now! But you can't move! You are strapped down!

Just a moment ago it felt so good. Now there is agony.

Then those giant hands pinch and clamp and crush your healthy, pure, innocent baby penis skin.

You tell them to stop in the only way you know how. You scream a long, shrill scream. You do everything you can to escape. Your head crashes from side to side, screaming, *No! No!*, wordlessly. You arch your back and tighten every muscle in your body.

The more you scream, the worse it gets. They pull on the newly separated, raw, bleeding tissue. Your heart races at a dangerous pace.

Then, they do something new. They cut and they cut. They cut that lovely part off. A king's ransom of good feelings — gone. It is gone. Gone. A precious piece of your perfect human body. Gone forever.

The pain is deafening, but no sound comes out of your mouth. You go limp, pass out.

"See," they say, "it didn't hurt him at all. He slept through the whole thing."

You lie in silent shock. No one protected you. No one cared. You were so alone. You were powerless. You were helpless to defend yourself. It was hopeless to try. No matter what you did, they just kept hurting you.

You are stunned. Frightened. Defeated.

This is how they welcome people to Planet Earth? This is how they treat people here? What kind of place is this? What do I need to do to survive here?

They wrap you up again in your blanket and carry you back

to a cold, flat, hard bed where you can only sleep. All energies spent, in vain. No matter what you did, they would not stop. You did everything you could to tell them to stop, but they did not see nor hear you. You lost everything.

For weeks after, you live in endless, excruciating pain. Urine, feces, ammonia, soaps and ointments, diapers, touch of any kind — even loving hugs — all serve to make you hurt again. You don't care to eat.

Some tortures are even worse than others... some mommies, nurses and nannies were told to swab the open wound with alcohol. And since they truly love you, they do it often — for your own good, of course.

They call you a "fussy" baby. They don't understand why you don't breast feed, why you scream and stiffen when someone picks you up to feed you. They don't know that your sleep is disturbed with nightmares, paralysis, attacks by giant monsters, visions of being eaten alive by wild animals. Unable to help yourself, unable to scream, unable to get the attention you need, unable to get help. Alone. So alone.

"What's wrong with my baby?"[5,6] your concerned mama asked, after your ordeal.

"Oh, it's nothing," sang the nurse. *"It's just his circumcision."*

THERE'S NOTHING THERE

Within a few days of John's question, *Why is a girl writing a book about circumcision?* I was ready to write a chapter about the anatomy of the foreskin and penis. I asked on the Intact-L list if someone could explain to me how it worked.

Someone responded with a suggestion that changed my life: "The anatomy of the female clitoris is identical to that of the male penis, only smaller."

I would never have guessed that!

I thought girls only had "innies" — but we have "outies" too? Neat!

I was so glad I found out! This promised to make it easier to research and write about the anatomy of the prepuce. I could learn about the foreskin from my own body.

I was enthralled by the idea of having a small replica of the penis and foreskin in my own anatomy.

How charming and convenient!

Now, where is this clitoris thing? I've never seen it before. A miniature penis? On a female? ... Where?

So, out came the 5X magnifying mirror. Out came a big bright lamp. I tested every corner of my apartment for privacy...

I would have been mortified if anyone caught me examining the space between my legs.

Mama would have killed me.

Finally, I found the perfect spot. Light, bright, but far enough away from the windows that faced the parking lot and the windows on the river side.

No one will see me here.

I looked at my private parts, hitherto pretty much secret, even from myself. They had never seemed interesting before. A bit bland and featureless, I had always thought.

But now! Surely they will be far more interesting than I'd remembered. Now I have a purpose — I can see how the foreskin works.

Or so I imagined.

I looked.

I thought, *There is nothing there.*

I brought in another lamp and looked again under better lighting.

There is still nothing there.

I tried another mirror. Nothing.

I looked and I looked and I looked.

Where is it?

I talked again to my friend who said those fated words suggesting the male-female similarity.

"Guess what, Ed! — I looked at myself and I don't know what you are talking about. I can't find anything. There's nothing there."

"That's impossible," he assured me. "Look again."

And so I did. But still, I saw nothing.

Ed said, "If it won't offend you, I'll send you some photos of other women. Then you will know what to look for on yourself."

The photos arrived. I looked at them. I looked at myself.

Now I was even more certain that there was nothing there. I got nervous — very nervous.

I'd never heard about little girls being circumcised. I'd never heard of it ever, in any way. And yet, with a little more research, I found it was true.

In the late 1800s and early 1900s A few obstreperous medical voices claimed masturbation was the root cause of hundreds of diseases. Both girls and boys were circumcised because both boys and girls touched themselves and adults devised all sorts of clever and torturous ways to torment children who touched themselves, including cutting genital parts off. Restraining devices, cages, alert caretakers, genital cutting and carbolic acid aimed at deterring and punishing children for masturbation were all justified under the umbrella of "disease prevention".

In the middle of the 20th century, clitorises were also surgically reduced or removed because of size. Martha Coventry wrote her story, in her excellent article "The Tyranny of the Esthetic: Surgery's Most Intimate Violation" in the Summer 1998 volume of *On The Issues,*

> Big clitorises aren't allowed in America. By big, I mean over three-eighths of an inch for newborns, about the size of a pencil eraser. Tiny penises, under one inch, aren't allowed either. A big clitoris is considered too capable of becoming alarmingly erect, and a tiny penis not quite capable enough.
> Such genitals are confounding to the strictly maintained and comforting social order in America today, which has

everyone believing that bodies come in only two ways: perfectly female and perfectly male. But genitals are surprisingly ambiguous.

One out of every 2,000 babies is born with genitals that don't elicit the automatic "It's a girl!" or "It's a boy!" Many more have genitals that are perceived as "masculinized" or "feminized," although the child's sex is not in doubt.

The American Academy of Pediatrics recommends surgically altering these children between the ages of six weeks and 15 months to fashion their bodies into something closer to perfection. Everyone can then breathe easier, except for the child, who may well spend the rest of her or his life trying to let the breath flow easy and full through the fear and shame created by such devastating surgery.

In his story, "Natural Causes" published in *DoubleTake Magazine* (Winter 1997), author Peter Feibleman told his mother's story,

> In 1916 a clitoridectomy was performed on my mother, at age five, to stop her from masturbating. The surgery was done at the request of her mother, not in Africa but in a fashionable area of Manhattan where she was born, at the office of a distinguished gynecologist whose fees were consonant with his fame; I first found about it in 1944 when I was fourteen, from my father, who explained it to me in detail as the reason for her wanting a divorce.
>
> Teenagers are more curious than considerate, and I went straight to my mother to find out if it was true. I remember that day better than most days because it was the first time I'd ever seen my mother cry. She confirmed the mutilation, denied that it was the reason for the divorce, and added that we would not discuss the matter again.
>
> At the time I believed her case was unique – that my mother had been singled out by some mysterious fate and mangled in an unthinkable way. But I was wrong, her case was far from unique, and a few years later in a fumbling effort to

confront my own fear about the subject, I began to seek the truth from medical men of my grandmother's vintage. One of them, a second-generation gynecologist then in his eighties, explained that the sexual mutilation of American women had been a lucrative industry in the United States from 1867 until at least 1927, and possibly much later – a thriving business few people spoke about afterward. In describing it, he told me more than I wanted to know at the time, and within a decade I'd mostly succeeded in putting the whole thing out of my mind.

And then I heard about little girls in Africa who were circumcised. We Americans called African circumcision, *Female Genital Mutilation* (FGM), much to the dismay of African women.

Then I met an angry, aggressive American woman in my town who remembered her circumcision at age three. After having three sons, she had a baby girl. Her daughter's anatomy was very different from her own — and unsettling memories began to return... a hospital corridor, three gurneys with bars like cribs, she and her two siblings, excruciating pain...

A Canadian woman told me that her mother chose to circumcise her so she would be "pretty".

Another woman in my town told me that as she was being prepared for an unrelated surgery, her husband and the doctor conferred in the corner of the room about amputating her clitoral hood. Why? For the same reason females are circumcised in Africa — to keep her from straying. They did not consult her. She was insulted that her husband would even think that she would be unfaithful. Their marriage did not endure for long.

Circumcision is an amorphous surgery, a panacea of sorts, achieving whatever end the circumciser claims. It is sold as both an enhancer and a diminisher of sexual pleasure... how versatile circumcision is! The same twofold benefits are touted for male circumcision, both increasing and decreasing sensitivity.

It's a cure for every complaint.

In 1996, a woman sued her ex-husband (a medical doctor) because he had conspired with her surgeon to circumcise her while she was under anesthesia for an unrelated surgery. In this case the doctor claimed it would increase her interest in sex.

She sued her ex, she said, so that women could stand up against all forms of rape.

"That's what it is," she said, *"surgical rape!* When my body parts were cut off and thrown away. If it had been done on a back street or in an alley, he'd be in jail. But because it was done in an operating room, *I'm supposed to be grateful?"*

Shortly after her court victory, female circumcision was made illegal in the USA. Female Genital Mutilation (FGM) has been outlawed in Britain, Canada, France, Sweden, Switzerland and the United States.

However, in 2000, I met a woman who went into a teaching hospital for work on her cervix and came out without a clitoris. Beware of men with knives, especially if they arrange for general anesthesiology when your friends had the same procedure performed with only a local painkiller.

My cell phone rang while I was out riding my bicycle. A woman in western Kansas had found me on the Internet. When she began talking about her clitoridectomy, I fell off the bike into the street. It had happened when she was in high school in Kansas and she had felt manipulated into it by the doctor. She wanted to sue the doctor, who was still alive at that time. Another very *angry* woman.

A woman in Florida told me about an episiotomy that had been forced on her by a female doctor who said, "Well! You don't want to *tear*, do you?" My friend was still in pain from that cut when her baby daughter was a year old. She was still unhealed and still angry. No doctor she talked to would treat her. They all told her to go back to her attending physician — the one who had cut her against her wishes.

I have spoken to numerous women about their genital cutting. None of them were happy with the procedures or the results; they all were angry... very, very angry.

Why do we imagine that men are angry for no good reason?

Another friend told me about her hysterectomy. When she visited Africa, she met a male doctor who daily dealt with the heart-wrenching life-threatening dilemma of women trying to give birth who had been both circumcised and infibulated (the vaginal opening is sewn shut to leave only a tiny hole). This doctor was disgusted to hear that an American doctor had removed both of my friend's ovaries without her consent.

Tonsillectomies, appendectomies, hysterectomies... the surgery of the day. Whatever is fashionable, whatever is profitable, whatever can be rationalized and sold...

And as this book is going to press, a mother of two young children, a woman I personally know, is undergoing a hysterectomy in 2010.

It seemed to me that doctors can be a little "knife-happy" — and especially around genitalia — both female and male, young and old. I began to understand why I had huge reservations about being on this planet.

In my youth, had I heard of female circumcision, I might

have thought of it as a grisly yet fascinating kinky quirk of igno-rant and superstitious tribes. But the scientifically sophisticated American medical protectors of women and children, defenders of human rights? Peddling unnecessary, ritualistic sexual surger-ies that alter people physically and mentally for life — to their detriment?

I seriously wonder how many people have been affected.

Something makes me want to do everything I can to shake people awake. Nobody deserves this kind of treatment... nobody... not even the worst of criminals. And yet they continue to take knives to the most vulnerable of all — women in labor and brand new babies.

And if doctors don't collect the pristine prepuce and the circumcision fee at birth, they work hard to justify circumcision later by themselves forcibly retracting the foreskin or instruct-ing parents to retract it and wash it with soap, until it develops adhesions or infections from the unnecessary tinkering and then requires surgical intervention.

Why, I ask, is there so much adult focus on little children's genitals? What is it all about? Obsession?

DOCTOR, DO I HAVE A CLITORIS?

What's a girl to do when she suspects she might have lost her clitoris? Find a doctor? That's the very last thing I felt inclined to do. I'd had an aversion to doctors my entire life. It wasn't easy for me to make an appointment to see a gynecologist.

I finally decided to see the most politically-correct and popular ob-gyn in town, a well-mannered, likable European-born man with a pleasant accent and a thriving holistic practice, the darling of the beautiful people.

We shook hands. I knew he was a busy man and we wouldn't have all day for polite banter, so I jumped right in.

"Doctor," I said, "do you have a foreskin?"

He looked more than a little surprised. "Why, yes, I do."

"That's good. Do you have many patients who have sexual problems?"

"Why, yes, I do."

"Do you ever ask them if their husbands have foreskins?"

"No. I never thought to do that. Why should I?"

"Well, you should. Most American men are circumcised. Without a foreskin, sex can be irritating and abrading." He looked shocked.

"Do you perform circumcisions, Doctor?"

"If the parents insist, I do," he said, "but I try to talk them out of it. There is no medical reason for it."

In my ideal world, he would have said, "No, I never do circumcisions under any circumstances," but he didn't. And I was here, so we got down to the work at hand.

Exit, doctor. Undress. Put on a silly paper smock. Knock, knock.

"Come in." Enter doctor and female chaperone carrying a small, handheld mirror.

The good doctor, in his charming accent, gave me a guided tour of my mysterious little private parts, poking here and there with a little pointer.

"This is the labia majora, labia minora ..."

He stayed politely, safely on the surface. He apparently thought I wanted an anatomy lesson. I guess I hadn't explained my purpose clearly.

So I said, "Thanks, Doc, but I know *where* the clitoris is supposed to be. What I really wanted to know is, *do I have one?* Do I have a clitoris or don't I?"

Looking puzzled, poking here and there, he finally put his finger on something and rubbed, a little too firmly. It was uncomfortable.

"There it is!" He declared triumphantly. "You have a teeny tiny little bitty clitoris — a *microscopic* clitoris. A *lot* of women have *teeny tiny little bitty clitorises. Nothing to worry about. You are normal,"* he smiled reassuringly. Charming.

"Thanks, Doc. I just wanted to know for sure."

But I was not altogether convinced. Exit doctor and female

chaperone. I dressed, paid my bill at the counter and left.

For days after the exam I had cramps extending into my entire abdomen from the spot the doctor had rubbed. I doubted his diagnosis.

I bought new, upgraded equipment: a brighter light and 10X magnification, but looking as hard as I could, I still could see nothing there. I wondered if there was something wrong with my eyes.

Next, I went to an optometrist, had my eyes tested, bought a pair of prescription eyeglasses and looked again, but I didn't see anything resembling a clitoris.

A few weeks later I went back to the doctor's office. I decided that I needed to pull back the labia for him. He hadn't really pulled the area apart as I did at home. Perhaps he hadn't seen what *wasn't* there because he was afraid of being too intrusive.

As usual, I didn't mince words. "Doctor, I had cramps for days after our last appointment. And I'm sorry, but I don't agree that I have a clitoris. This time I am going to show you myself what *isn't* there."

More undressing. Same scene all over again. Trusty chaperone standing behind him, I pulled back the skin and made the area where the clitoris should be, clear and unobstructed, for easy viewing. He looked sincerely puzzled.

"Did you know, Doctor," I said, "that Blue Cross Blue Shield insurance paid for clitoridectomies in the United States until 1977?"

His shocked expression told me all I needed to know. That embarrassing chapter of medical history had been left out of his textbooks. Even authors of the most scholarly books about the history of circumcision don't know how long female genital mutilation endured in the USA. The history of female circumcision here has been a well-guarded secret, especially from its victims.

Exit doctor and trusty chaperone. I dressed and began to leave. I was by now even more convinced that I had no clitoris, not even an itty bitty one — just scar tissue, a nerve bundle and phantom pain. And it was clear in my mind that the doctor agreed.

As I walked down the hall to leave, he came running after me. "Wait! Wait! This is for you!"

What's this? A newspaper article opposing routine infant medical circumcision. It was written by the doctor himself, years before, when he had studied medicine in Canada.

"You can take this with you," he said. "There will be no charge for today."

I thought it would be helpful to have my medical records from childhood. The doctor's staff tried to get them, but couldn't. I called the hospital in Kansas City. "We don't keep records for more than ten years," said the voice on the phone.

How does the medical system know whether procedures work if they don't keep records and follow up on patients? The same way that religions know that their rites and rituals work to get their followers to heaven?

"Science is a wonderful thing," said Mark Twain in *Life on the Mississippi*. "One gets such wholesale return of conjecture for such a trifling investment of fact."

Does America have "evidence-based medicine"? Or is medicine in America, like Doctor Robert Mendelsohn said in his book *Confessions of a Medical Heretic* — a religion of sorts, a belief system, where doctors are the priests, nurses are the nuns, surgery is the ritual and medicines are the sacraments, the AMA is the Vatican, and questioners are heretics?

Has medicine usurped religion's function as mediator of morals, taking the religious ritual of circumcision and turning it into a routine medical procedure — and profit center — without truly scientific evidence that it helps or harms, but just a few sketchy studies turned into statistics? Appears it might have done just that. It's clear there needs to be objective, unbiased research performed on the long-term physical, mental and emotional effects of genital alteration on both women and men.

Not even one more child should be cut until it is proved safe to his body, mind and social environment.

After I found out about my circumcision, I shyly joined the internet mailing list, Restore, where almost a thousand men supported one another as they diligently worked on slowly regrowing their foreskins, using a variety of methods: manual tugging, taping with weights, o-rings and bicycle pumps.

When I shared my story, one man wrote that in his childhood he had lived next door to a woman from Nigeria. He and the other children in the neighborhood would gather on her porch on long summer evenings and she would tell them stories about life in Africa. She told them she had been circumcised. She also told them how she had restored her clitoris, once she moved to America. He explained the procedure she used to me.

So I returned to the medical clinic, confident that the good doctor would coach me safely through the process, but when I mentioned the purpose of my visit, his face turned bright red. He began sweating, and talking fast.

"*You are obsessing!*" he said. "You have a clitoris. You have a teeny tiny, little bitty, microscopic clitoris. *Stop thinking about it!*" He then proceeded to lecture me about getting a pap smear and a mammogram.

Now, I was the one who was shocked!

You have a clitoris… ?

Did he really say that? I thought he had agreed on my second visit that there was no clitoris. What a waste of my time! I couldn't believe he said that — *You are obsessing… ?* Back to square one!

I understood better now what the men on the Restore list said about doctors — both physicians and psychiatrists — accusing them of "obsessing" when they express concern about their circumcisions. Here I was hearing the exact same words from the good doctor. Was this phrase used by doctors everywhere to avoid medical accountability? *You are obsessing.* Was this an occasion of a medical cover-up?

If I had asked him about a breast implant or reconstruction, what would he have said? Surely not that I was obsessing. Surely, he would have been very helpful.

If there has been preoccupation or obsession around circumcision, then it has been on the part of the medical system, not its tiny victims. Children do not seek out circumcision. But doctors have aggressively sold parents on it. An effective advertising campaign has been waged over the past century to remove healthy skin from children's genitals.

The public relations machine that drummed up the excuses

for circumcision have sold genital cutting like Brylcreem®, a hair styling gel.

"The gals will all pursue ya!" Look like dad? Locker room teasing? Girls prefer it? "Effortless!"

Brylcreem ads sound a lot like circumcision ads: "neater, cleaner, easier, cuter." And then there's the claim that circumcision is "healthier"? Is that true?

Not when you study the facts.

Doctors walk in lock step when it comes to selling circumcision to parents. They make light of it. *It doesn't hurt,* they say. *Babies don't feel pain.* They make circumcision sound as pleasant as a walk in the park. They gloss over the dangers and drawbacks. They neglect to tell parents how cutting human genitals can damage bodies and that even deaths occur for the sake of this cosmetic surgery.

Many doctors have blocked their ears to the screams of babies as they performed circumcisions. But those babies are adults now. Dissatisfied adult voices grow louder and stronger every day. Many tiny patients from the past, who are now grown people, are not as pleased with their circumcision scars as the doctor was with his fee. Some of those children have already sued and have won cases. Surely there will be many more in the future. I wish my doctor was alive. He would see a courtroom.

Obsessing, indeed!

Quite logically, no one should have to consult a doctor about whether or not they have a clitoris. Neither I nor any of my brothers or sisters should have to talk about our distress over circumcision. No one should have to be restoring a clitoris or a foreskin. No one's genitals should have been altered. Everyone should have natural bodies with sexual organs, intact. No one should have been surgically raped, tortured.

Circumcision is a form of socially-sanctioned childhood sexual abuse. Medical denial is another layer of abuse.

Honest accountability needs to occur. An end to the practice and a genuine apology to the people of the USA could heal hearts and prevent lawsuits.

Yes, Jesse, something awful did happen to me. It did resemble your ex-wife's childhood sexual abuse. And a doctor did it.

ALL THAT'S LEFT IS A SCAR

I gave up on the gynecologist and decided to buy a digital microscope that attached to my computer so I could determine for myself in the comfort of my own home whether or not I had a clitoris.

Bought it. Took it home. Pulled out my trusty mirror and lamp. Plugged the microscope into my computer. Took off my clothes from the waist down. Got down on the floor and began to point and click.

Though I was flexible, this job was not as easy as I had hoped. I had to juggle several different factors at once. I needed to shoot close-up pictures of the area between my legs, where I could not see and light never entered… I needed to be close but not too close… Focusing was tricky… Making sure the right area was lit… The computer screen was too dark, upside down and backwards… The lens changed focus at the slightest touch…

I twisted and turned in every direction until I was dazed, dizzy and exhausted. Thank goodness I was already on the floor so I didn't have far to fall.

This was clearly one of the most difficult tasks I'd ever

attempted. The tiniest movement caused me to lose the light, object and focus. It was a huge challenge to think backward and upside down in three dimensions. Clicking the button on the hand-held microscope blurred nearly every shot. All I could see was endless, glossy, bright pink mucousal tissue, similar to the inside of my mouth or under my eyelid. What was what? I couldn't tell. Such mysterious territory.

I gave up.

Although I'd hoped to complete this project on a low budget, it became obvious I really should have bought the additional lens — the expensive one. It could shoot beneath the reflective surface of the skin, beyond the pink! That is what I needed; exactly what was required.

Nervously clutching my checkbook, I returned to the store to buy the lens with the special polarized filter.

Home, naked on the floor again — *success at last!*

Where the clitoris used to be was just a clear, vivid *scar*, a perfectly mechanical V-shaped scar. No wonder I got cramps when the doctor rubbed that area. No wonder I never liked to have that part of my body touched by anyone, not even myself. It was just scar tissue. What was designed for pleasure was instead *phantom pain*.

Exploring further with the same lens, I then found a notch missing from my labia where hard, sharp metal had obviously met soft, sensitive skin. I felt sick to my stomach. *Crisp V-shapes and sharp 90-degree angles are not found in nature, not found on natural, intact human bodies.* I was saddened by this graphic evidence. It went beyond my expectations.

My friend Janice came to visit a few days later. I showed her the photos. "Yes," she said, "that's obviously a cut. I wonder why the V–shape? You can see where the tissue doesn't match up on either side of the V."

Looking closer, I saw she was right. It was clear that skin texture, blood vessels and nerves — had all been disrupted. *No wonder it had always felt jammed up in that spot.*

Later I found a 1959 medical journal article in *GP*, written by Dr. W. G. Rathmann: "Female Circumcision: Indications and a New Technique". Rathmann shamelessly promoted a barbaric "new, improved" tool used to clamp and amputate the clitoris and its hood. It looks, quite frankly, like a pair of pliers.

I wonder how many of these tools were sold and I wonder how many other women in the United States — *like me* — had been genitally altered with it. I wonder how many — *like me* — *didn't know and never would guess!*

Is it possible Mama was circumcised? Female genital surgery was peddled in those days for adult women as well as children. If Mama had also been circumcised that would explain her impatience, irritability and lack of interest in sex. Perhaps that is what she meant when she said, "They *cut* me!"

You want him to look like his father, don't you! "Like father like son" is a standard hospital sales pitch for routine infant male circumcision. If Mama had also been circumcised, she may have fallen for the same sales tactic. "Like mother, like daughter."

When I was in college, I was married and chronically sexually frustrated. I had no idea what an orgasm was. I became unhappy, impatient and irritable, much like Mama had been when I was a child. I wondered even in those days if it could have been sexual frustration that fueled her anger.

I once heard Daddy complain, *"I bought this box of condoms weeks ago and I still have some left!"*

"You want her to look like you — don't you!"

Whenever I'd asked Mama about my birth, she never answered my question. Instead, she responded with a vacant look and repeated, "They cut me… They cut me…" She went into a state of shock every time I asked, seeming to revisit something awful from the past.

Her labor had been prolonged, as are all births when women are forced to lie flat on hospital beds. Indentations in my skull witness to forceps use. It is likely Mama's vaginal opening was cut to facilitate my birth. But could she have been circumcised?

Mama has passed away, as have both her husbands and the doctor who delivered me, so I will never know exactly where they cut her or why. Whatever they cut, it was obvious that Mama still suffered trauma due to it many years later.

I awoke with this little ditty in my head. How many millions could claim it as their own?

I did the very best I could
to tell them
they were hurting me.
If they had heard,
they would have stopped,
but children
are to be seen and not heard.
And so they just kept cutting...
and cutting...

Please listen.

EXAMINATION
BY AN EXPERT WITNESS

A year or so had passed since the doctor visits ended and the microscope revealed the V-shaped scar. Visiting Marilyn Milos of the National Organization of Circumcision Information Resource Centers (NOCIRC), I told her what I had learned so far about my missing clitoris.

She cried. I was grateful, but it would still be years before my own tears would fall.

"Have you seen this book?" she asked, pulling a slim volume from her library shelves.

Femalia, a photo essay by Joani Blank, illustrating a wide variety of vulva (external female genitalia). Vulva all look different, but are similar in their gracefulness in their natural state.

A few months later I took a month-long class and the hostess for my stay in California was (coincidentally) an ob-gyn nurse who performed in-home wellness checks on new mothers and babies. She was one of several ob-gyn nurses I have met since I learned what had happened to me. None were aware of clitoridectomy in the USA until I mentioned it. It is something they don't want to believe and I certainly don't blame them; it certainly doesn't fit the image the medical profession wants to maintain.

The day before I drove back home, I attended a NOCIRC meeting in Berkeley, where I met Norma. Norma is a nurse, who for over twenty years had been part of a team of medical professionals who performed a very special function at the University of California, San Francisco School of Medicine. The team members — both male and female — used their own bodies to train medical students to perform gentle, respectful, professional genital exams.

I had heard of this program a couple of years earlier, so I already had tremendous respect for her work.

When Norma offered to examine me, I hesitated. I had always been leery of letting anyone near me. I offered to show her the photos I'd taken with the microscope. She said she wouldn't be able to tell much from photos.

It didn't take me long to weigh the pros and cons and realize that nowhere in all the world would I ever find a more qualified person to examine me. What a rare opportunity this was, given Norma's experience. So I agreed to the exam and we disappeared for a few minutes into another room.

As she would with her medical students, Norma was kind enough to show me her own normal, external, female genitalia. I was grateful to have already been introduced to normal vulva by Ed's photos and Marilyn's book *Femalia*, otherwise I would have been utterly shocked by the differences between Norma's body and mine.

Although there is a wide range of normal genital anatomy, it would have been obvious to the most casual observer that

Norma had intact genitalia and I did not. Her labia were elegant and flowing like flower petals. Mine were stubs. Her clitoris and hood were healthy — and yes, similar to male anatomy, only smaller. My body had nothing there.

Her visual exam confirmed that I had not only lost significant portions of my labia, but also the clitoral hood and the entire clitoris.

A few short weeks after my return home, by chance I met the good doctor, in a bookstore. We had a short chat and I told him about Norma, her credentials, the exam and her conclusion. This time it was my turn to shake with emotion.

"Once women read my book, Doctor, there may be a considerable number who will find they were circumcised. And when they come to you, I hope you will treat them with respect."

He listened carefully. I was grateful at that time to imagine I had been heard. I nurtured that illusion for several years.

However, in 2009 I discovered that a limb regeneration process I had read about in 2004 was finally available to the public. I called the ACell company and since their product is available only by prescription, I asked them to send their information to the good doctor.

A week later, the doctor called me and began again where he had left off years before — insisting that I get a pap smear and mammography. I said, "Thank you, but no thank you. I think I'll find someone else to help me."

YOUR MOTHER LET THEM
DO THAT TO YOU?

"Your mother let them *do* that to you?"

I could tell by the tone of her voice that Gert would never have allowed anyone to do that to her daughters. Her honest horror hit my heart and tears finally escaped for the first time since I'd discovered the scars.

I began to question everything...

- How could female genital circumcision have happened to a little white Anglo-Saxon protestant girl in the United States of America?

- What kind of parents would have allowed it? What on earth could they have been thinking?

- What kind of doctor would do such a thing? What kind of medical system advocates for genital mutilation?

- What were the prevailing social attitudes?

- What other forms of genital mutilation are still common in the USA... and why?

My parents divorced in 1971. Daddy died in 1982 and Mama died in 1997, so I could not ask them questions.

I spoke to my mother's friends and family but they didn't remember anything. All the doctors, teachers and school principals were long ago dead. Hospitals, I learned, keep records for only ten years, so there are no medical records of my birth and childhood.

It took me years to piece it all together. Thank goodness I had read a lot of Nancy Drew and Sherlock Holmes mystery novels in my youth.

WHERE DID THE SMILE GO?

I always giggle when I look at photos of myself as a little girl. From birth through kindergarten, I had the same easy, wide, genuine, honest smile... innocent, joyful, alive, sparkling eyes. That child was comfortable in her body: confident, saucy, flirtatious, genuine, grounded, simple, spontaneous, *happy!*

I have experimented and tried to smile like the child in these photos. It's not easy after you've forgotten how.

The smile in the first four photos here uses all the muscles in the face and scalp: mouth, nose, eyes, all the way around, into the center of the skull. There's something authentic about that smile. It is a total smile.

But then, something changed.

THE RAPE OF INNOCENCE

The photo on the left, below, is from kindergarten. The photo on the right is from first grade.

Compare the smiles, one year apart.

The kindergarten smile is like my earlier smiles on the previous page.

But the first grade smile is qualitatively different. To smile that smile, all you have to do is pull the corner of your mouth to one side with a couple of jaw muscles.

This is what I call a "lipstick" smile. It's a forced smile. It's more like a grimace. It's a *Say cheese!* smile. A slick, quick, obligatory smile. It's not a real smile at all.

What do you think? Do you see the difference too? The first grade photo never made me giggle. Instead, it made me wonder.

What happened? What happened to the spontaneity? What happened to the light in her eyes? What happened between kindergarten (relaxed, perky and free on the left) — and first grade (sour and dour, cynical and withdrawn, posed and closed on the right)?

Something terrible happened to that little girl.

The younger girl says, "I like me! I like you!" The new one says, "Go away! Don't touch me!"

The younger girl is grounded, balanced, breathing. The older girl is teetering, not breathing.

The first grade photo is the beginning of all my grown up

photos. After that, there were only grim lipstick smiles.

What happened to that little girl? Why did the joy turn to anger? Defiance? Resentment? What happened? The girl on the right wishes she was dead.

The new Patricia trusted no one. She pulled and pushed everyone away: family, friends, relationships, and even opportunities to have a family of her own. She lost herself for a long, long time.

I wore my Sherlock Holmes hat for a good thirty years, trying to figure out how, when and where the aliveness was lost. I tried everything I could think of to regain it, yet I was among the walking dead — *until I realized I had been circumcised and the buried trauma had been running my life!*

After I lost the battle for my clitoris, I lost my smile and my heart. The song left my soul. Yes, it all made sense.

When I finally found out, it was as if a great, huge, heavy, dark cloud lifted and I could breathe again. Healing began. And it took a while, but now my smile is returning.

If I think about it too long, I begin to wonder what kind of life I would have had if I'd not been circumcised. Thinking about it makes my throat tighten and my heart hurt. How very different things might have been.

SMILING BABIES

Mothers used to be told that infants don't smile until they are six or eight weeks old. That's true of newborns in hospitals. On the Internet I saw a video of a newborn smiling. The doctors and nurses had gathered around to watch. They were astounded. They'd never seen a newborn smile. Babies born in hospitals cry; they do not smile. This was one in a million.

But babies born gently smile within hours or days, not weeks. Frederick Leboyer's 1975 book and movie *Birth without Violence* advocated soft lights, a quiet environment, warm water and gentle handling. Naturally born babies look like happy little baby buddhas.

Natural, happy, healthy, knife- and drug-free should be the gold standard of every birth.

The video, *Birth As We Know It*, clearly illustrates both problem and solution. It contrasts babies born naturally in safe warm water lakes or at home — alert, awake, smiling and immediately responsive — with babies born in fear, in violent, raucous, hospital circus tent atmospheres — pulled squalling out of a drugged mother or cut from the womb, and then abruptly separated from both placenta and mother right after birth for the all-important fear-based medical routine.

And to top it off, the healthy genitals of baby boys are cut.

So is it any wonder babies born in hospitals do not smile for weeks or months?

WHAT ABOUT OTHERS?

Curious about other children's photos, I have peeked at hospital's birth announcements on the Internet. Some are peaceful. Others look as if they have been raped, or even worse. I have no way of knowing for sure who was violated by circumcision and who was not but it should not be difficult to perform such a study.

I wish gentle, kind treatment for all children.

SOCIETY IN DENIAL

In his books, psychologist Ron Goldman discusses the devastating effects of circumcision on the human psyche of both the child and the adult spectators or participants. He reports a reaction he has noticed after a ritual circumcision... Although the child *screamed* throughout the bris, the adults in attendance told each other that the baby *did not cry.*

Not only do children forget the horror, adults want to forget it too. Memory can be selective and faulty. People lie to themselves and each other. Circumcising societies have been in denial for a very long time now.

"Circumcision is not mutilation," they say. "It's medicine." "Circumcision *is* my religion." "It's not torture... babies don't feel a thing." "There is something wrong with *you* if you think cutting children's genitals hurts them."

Is it time yet for us to grow up and tell the truth?

Some say that babies sleep through their circumcisions.

Now that's a good one. But I can't imagine it and I don't believe it. Why? *Because it's not true.*

It's *not* sleep. If children do not scream when they are being cut, is it because the knife doesn't hurt them? Are they really sleeping through it? Or are they in such a deep state of shock that they cannot scream? I used to have nightmares in which I was so terrified that, try with all my might, I could not scream. Adrenalin, the fear hormone, creates fight, flight *and* freeze responses. Passing out is a way out of a threatening situation.

There are people who suffer from circumcision fetish and may have themselves circumcised numerous times until they achieve a certain, fashionable "high, tight cut", but what normal adult would allow anyone near their own genitals with a knife?

Think about it. Can you imagine yourself sleeping while someone carves up your genitals? I can't. Can you imagine passing out from the pain and the terror? I can. That is the "sleep" of babies being circumcised. It is the baby's attempt to escape.

Medical school students were once taught the old wives tale, "Babies don't feel pain." Students who answered "True" to the statement, "Circumcision hurts babies" failed their exam. But real research has found that babies are exquisitely aware and feel more acutely than adults.

It is understandable that doctors may need to block out the screams of patients they are working on in emergency situations with burn patients, broken arms, etc. But with circumcision, the doctor is inflicting unnecessary pain on a tiny victim who has no words nor ability to walk away. A baby can only scream or pass out. Doctors need to learn that in baby language, screams mean, *"No! Stop! Don't do that!"*

Doctors need a sensitivity training in which they are shown over and over again movies of babies being circumcised until each one understands in every cell of his or her being that, yes indeed, babies have very acute senses. Babies feel pain. Babies communicate their distress quite eloquently, in a variety of ways. This will be clear to anyone who is paying attention.

Doctors also need education about the function of the foreskin, and the health of intact men around the world. They also need education about how beautifully nature designed sex to work. Since they do not have a foreskin, they do not know how valuable it is.

> A man comes out of the lavatory and says, "Ah! That was great! A good dump can be better than sex!"
> His friend looks at him wide-eyed. "Man, either I don't know how to sh-t or you don't know how to f-ck!"

This joke illustrates the cognitive gap between a circumcised man and an intact man. The circumcised man equates sex with defecation. The intact man, with all his body parts, knows that sex is a far superior experience. But neither understands their different perceptions have to do with altered genitalia.

Since most doctors are circumcised, they have no concept of what they are depriving their tiny patients of as they merrily cut away the most sensitive part of the male anatomy. Much education is needed to replace this huge gap in medical training.

Doctors also need to know research shows that babies undergoing circumcision have three to four times the cortisol levels, their heartbeat is 50% above the baseline, and that babies are *more* aware of pain than adults. A physician wrote that, subjecting an adult to the same practice would be "unfathomable".

A child will do anything and everything possible to avoid the pain of circumcision. If a child is quiet, it is because to freeze is the only option he has at the time. He is not asleep, he has left his body. He has passed out, dissociated.

Dissociation is a temporary mental escape from unbearable trauma. Often there will be a memory gap surrounding the experience. Trauma produces amnesia. Of course, most of us *would* want to forget an incident like that.

If a stranger broke into our homes and handled and cut our children's genitals in the same way that circumcisers do, we would not tolerate it for a moment. We would call them *perverts* and *child molesters*, throw them in jail and never let them out. But for some reason we allow our children to be "circumcised". We are, as a society, hypnotized by white coats, stethoscopes and euphemisms.

"If it had been done on a back street or in an alley, he'd be in jail. But because it was done in an operating room, *I'm supposed to be grateful?*"

All human beings are blind people.

We do not see our children struggling to escape. We do not hear their screams as cries for help. We do not act on our natural instincts to protect them from harm.

Richard Matteoli, in his book *The Munchausen Complex: Socialization of Violence and Abuse,* explores the dishonest religious and social imperatives that mandate circumcision, the psychological aberrations involved, the legal and criminal implications.

When acting out of their own unhealed pain, human beings are not only blind, they can be malevolent. They do things to helpless children that they would not wish to have done to themselves. Tie an adult who advocates or performs circumcisions to a table, bring a knife to their genitals and they will be begging for mercy. Penetrate the flesh and they will be screaming from the pain. Yet they laugh about a child being cut or impatiently dismiss the complaints of an adult who regrets having been circumcised.

What circumcision steals from its tiny victim is far more than a body part. Circumcision steals innocence, trust, peace of mind. The ability to relax is lost. Tension is fused to every muscle of the body. The child and the adult he becomes is uncomfortably hypervigilant, alert and always on the lookout for more pain and betrayal. It's difficult for him or her to really get emotionally close to anyone. They call circumcised children "fussy".

One woman told me, "My son doesn't *like* people."

On his web site, Ronald Goldman wrote that some mothers and nurses who contacted the Circumcision Resource Center noted behavior changes. One obstetrical nurse who has seen many circumcised infants before they go home, reported,

> When you lay them on their stomachs they scream. When their diaper is wet they scream. Normally, they don't scream if their diaper is wet. Baby boys who are not circumcised do not scream like that. The circumcised babies are more irritable, and they nurse poorly.

Mothers reported that their infants changed temperament after the circumcision, cried for extended periods at home, and seemed inconsolable. Behavioral changes, including sleeping and eating, were observed in 90% of cases. Researchers at Harvard Medical School and Children's Hospital in Boston noted changes in sleep patterns, activity level, irritability, and mother-infant interaction.

Trust is lost: trust in mother, trust in father, trust in doctors. If the child forgets specifically who hurt him or her, then ultimately he or she will generalize that mistrust and be suspicious of the motives of all women or all men, all doctors, all adults, all authority figures. He or she loses faith in the goodness of life.

Quality of life: joy, happiness, trust, the will to live, peace, concentration, confidence, the ability to breathe deeply, fully and freely — all may be diminished. And for what? For the sake of social conformity? For the sake of superstition? For the sake of a few bucks?

How long will we be able to fool ourselves that no damage has been done?

What happens to a child's mind after losing such an important battle? Can you imagine men in America minus the circumcision trauma?

Tom, what do you think it did to your mind when they circumcised you?

There are only three cultures that circumcise their young and they are Jews, English-speaking Christians and Muslims.

Is it a coincidence that those three cultures are at war in the Middle East? Is it a coincidence we three groups frighten ourselves, one another and the entire world? Does the circumcision trauma make us feel we have to protect ourselves by fighting the world?

Is it any wonder that in the eyes of other cultures, we are extremely violent and destructive?

They fear us.

NOTHING IS IRRATIONAL
WHEN ALL THE FACTS ARE KNOWN

When people find out I had a clitoridectomy, many of them ask, *Weren't you angry when you found out?*

They expect me to say, *Yes!*

But I must tell the truth. The answer is, *No.*

I was angry *until* I found out. *After* I found out, I could at last let go of my fear and anger and *breathe* again. I have been healthier and happier every year since my discovery.

It was a relief to discover my anger was not irrational, that it had a cause. I had been reliving feelings of powerlessness from an overwhelming event. As long as the terror was buried, I had no words for it, only nightmares. Circumcision had surely become a forbidden word in our house as soon as it happened.

Forgive and forget, forgive and forget was my mother's litany.

I was poisoned for decades by feelings of fear, anger, grief and loss that literally made me ill. I had no idea where it had come from.

Mama had often said that my anger was "uncalled for" and it certainly must have seemed that way to the casual observer. Now, in hindsight, in the context of post-traumatic stress disorder (PTSD) due to clitoridectomy, my history makes perfect sense.

In the emotional desert we called "home" there would have been no comforting, no holding, no apology, but there would have been denial.

Nothing happened! Stop crying! It didn't hurt! Don't talk about it!

With crystal clarity I remember one specific moment when I stood my ground, fist in the air. She said, *Don't you raise your hand like that at me, young lady.*

I suspect that was shortly after the circumcision. When I raised my hand, my heart fell. I remember crying inside, *This isn't me!* But I felt certain that if I didn't learn to protect myself in what I had come to perceive as a very hostile world, I would surely die. I became an angry little girl who grew into an angry woman, wanting to be dead, yet intent on survival.

When I was 35, I participated in a workshop exercise where a few people would hold one person down to make them feel powerless for several seconds so he or she could then struggle to get loose. This was to make them realize they actually were powerful, not powerless.

When it came my turn, we were all amazed at my strength and fury. It required several strong men to hold me down. Along with the urge to push and kick, I also screamed, *Go away! I hate you! Leave me alone! Don't touch me!* Those words must have been the words I screamed at the doctor and my mother.

Through my childhood and adulthood, since the memory of the event was lost yet the terror persisted, those thoughts and words often surfaced at the wrong time with the wrong people — people I wanted to be close to — pushing them away.

Squeeze a balloon in one area and it pops out somewhere else. Unresolved feelings have to go somewhere. In my case, fear and grief turned to rage and depression. It is a miracle that I didn't become an alcoholic or a drug addict.

Whenever Mama hurt me, she would always say harshly, *That didn't hurt*! There was never a lot of room for discussion. I was always wrong. Her words were easy to predict, like the mother rabbit in a Matt Groening cartoon:

- Forgive and forget.
- That didn't hurt.
- Don't tell anyone.
- Don't cry or I'll give you something to cry about.
- What you think doesn't matter.
- Children should be seen and not heard.

If only we could have talked about the final thing she had said that day in the country with Tom and Nick, *You never were the same after your surgery*.

If only I had said more than, *You mean my tonsillectomy?* If only I had asked *What do you mean, my "surgery"?... Can you say more about that?*

I believe that was as close as Mama ever came to telling me about the clitoridectomy. If only I had known. Perhaps the healing would have occurred much sooner.

On a conscious level the circumcision assault had been forgotten, but it was glued to every cell of the subconscious. My body told the tale eloquently: pimples and stomach aches, sore throats, migraine headaches, chronic foot, neck and back pain, so much pain.

The body told the story of a huge volcano of rage, fury, sorrow and grief, a bottomless pit of loneliness and helplessness always seething and surging, buried and bursting out at inopportune times, exaggerated in view of current situations. I had no idea why. *This isn't me!*

No one, including me, could understand my angst. Friends, school counselors, co-workers, workshop conductors. For years I fought an invisible enemy: kicking, fighting, screaming with an urgent need to escape.

I look around now and see circumcised men in the same situation as I was. And nobody understands what they went through as tiny babies.

Go away! Leave me alone! Don't touch me! This isn't me!

How tragic that those words often came when someone dear came too near for comfort. Those words were undoubtedly the words I might have said to the people who came too close, who touched me without my permission, overpowered and hurt me. *How dare you! I hate you!*

I lost that battle! The adults won and I lost. Millions upon millions of little boys have lost that same battle and appear to act out the same scenario. *Go away! Leave me alone! This isn't me!*

The most haunting picture I have in my mind's eye, is of the mending process. Curled up in a tight little ball, the little girl who had long ago been me, was inconsolable. *Don't touch me!*

Her pain was excruciating, both physical and emotional. She could not believe anyone would hurt her in that way. She felt utterly bereft, betrayed. She could not believe that her good-feeling part had been cut away. Without that part of her body, she could not comfort herself in times of trouble and despair. Her comfort was gone forever. *Nobody loves me.*

Eventually, through the days and weeks, the wound healed, crusted and scabbed and scarred and knit together skin and muscles and nerves and blood vessels. *The smile was gone.*

Nature did what it could to put my body back together. But my former happy lightheartedness turned to sorrow and grief and my warmth turned cold and icy. Fears and tears froze into an impenetrable wall. Rigid, hard, harsh, angry feelings plagued my life and they erupted in behaviors that I never consciously understood. Consequently, I hated myself. Forgotten trauma leads to "uncalled for" acting out, dramatization. What a mystery i was! *You never were the same after your surgery.*

So no, I was not at all angry to find out. Surprised, yes, but mostly relieved to know that there was logic behind what I had thought before was irrational. Without the circumcision information, my life hadn't made sense — and now it finally did.

I have learned from many clients that when all the facts are known, nothing is irrational and everything can be healed. All fear can be released.

The little girl who went through that ordeal must have been terrified. She had many mysterious feelings too big for a little girl to hold: betrayal, violation, humiliation, hopelessness, abandonment, dread. She felt utterly unloved. All I can do now is to love her, forgive her and have tremendous compassion for her, in spite of her misadventures. She was doing the best she could under the circumstances.

It all made so much more sense once all the facts were

known. Suddenly I had a handle on a pivotal event. I could work with it, massage it, melt it, soften it, discharge it, release it and begin to breathe again.

So the undoing began. The letting go. Muscles in my shoulders and neck released ancient knots. I breathed more deeply, fully, freely, easily — oxygen reached new areas of my lungs. My energy returned. *God's will for you is perfect happiness.*

I no longer felt a need to run scared. I settled down, bought a home, planted a garden where chickens tended to the bugs and dug up the earth for worms. Deer sleep at the side of my house.

My smile is not altogether restored, but it comes far more easily now and it is genuine when it does. There's love and warmth behind it now. It's no longer just a lipstick smile.

At last I knew who I had been angry with and why. At last I knew where to direct my energy — at a misguided social system that unnecessarily sheds the blood of its innocent, helpless children.

MY FAMILY

MAMA

One thing you need to know about Mama is that she was *thorough.* Her whole family was. When we visited Mama's sister, Aunt Polly, in England, she would clean the ashtray as soon as Mama dropped an ash in it. She'd rush in with a brush to swish the toilet as soon as it was flushed.

Mama wasn't the most fastidious housekeeper but she certainly overdid things. She always said *If a little is good, a lot is even better.* Adding twice the amount of recommended spices, she once made a corned beef that only she could eat.

She approached child rearing with the same rigor. She had a burning desire to parent *perfectly.* And like most new mothers, she wanted her first child to be *perfect.*

She'd say, *Anything worth doing, is worth doing right* or *If it isn't worth doing right, it isn't worth doing at all.*

Another thing you need to know about Mama is that, she loved doctors. She loved the word, *doctor.* When she said, *doctor,* she said it with reverence. In her mind, doctors were gods. She was putty in their hands. To be fair, any authority figure, the Queen of England, medical doctors, teachers, rich people, romance — placed her into a waking trance — she would become utterly awestruck. That glazed look would come over her. She would dance around our house and sing,

> I'm the sheik of Araby... your love belongs to me... At night where you're asleep, into your tent I'll creep. The sun that shines above will light our way to love. You rule this world with me, I'm the sheik of Araby.

Although she didn't have access to Arabian sheiks or British royalty, she could readily see doctors by being sick or by having an ailing child. She may have been overly fond of doctors, or overly lonely. Mama was always happy to see a doctor and she would do anything a doctor suggested. She was honored to be at their service.

In the way that people who pay to hobnob with doctors do, she loved to recite her symptoms, the diagnoses and the names of all the medicines she was prescribed. She liked to say big words like es-o-pha-go-gas-tro-du-o-de-no-scop-ee or art-e-o-art-rite-us in her British accent with a mischievous smile.

At age 73, Mama had survived one bout with cancer and chemotherapy. She lost her hair but was strong and on her way to complete recovery when the doctor said there was something he could not identify — a dark spot on an x-ray of her skull. He recommended "just for good measure" a second round of che-motherapy — *and unfortunately she agreed to it!* The result was death from heart failure, one of the unfortunate side effects of chemotherapy. I suspect she may be alive today if she had not been so characteristically thorough... and so well insured.

In my youth, I'd imagined that my clever Mama had

originated all the snappy little phrases she used to shame and scold me. But Matt Groening's cartoon *Life in Hell* helped me understand that she had not.

In sixteen frames of one cartoon, a funny, stunned bunny with big, expressive ears reeled in shock sixteen times from sixteen of Mama's clichés. I could almost hear her sing-song voice repeating them in that mocking tone of voice. The bunny rabbit in shock was me.

I kept that cartoon. It helped me put Mama's scoldings into perspective. She was just passing down what she had learned from her own mother or father.

At some point, a psychiatrist suggested not to refer to her as *my mother,* but instead to call her *Mary.* I did that for a while, and it too helped me gain some distance and objectivity.

Teasing was Mama's way of letting me know she cared, but to a small child, it didn't feel very loving. A hug might have said it better. And if teasing wasn't bad enough, she tucked me in at night with thoughts that now sound very morbid. I can understand why I was hesitant to go to bed and why I often laid awake long hours in the middle of the night…

> *Now I lay me down to sleep,*
> *I pray the Lord my soul to keep.*
> *If I should die before I wake,*
> *I pray the Lord my soul to take.*

Throughout the days she often sang me this little ditty:

> *Nobody likes me, everybody hates me.*
> *I'm goin' down the garden to eat worms.*
> *Long thin slimy ones, short fat fuzzy ones,*
> *Ooey gooey, ooey gooey worms.*

I have a black and white photo of Mama cutting a birthday cake for a group of beautiful, young, English "war brides" aboard the Queen Mary ocean liner. Barbara, the woman on her right, remained a lifelong friend.

Yes, in March of 1946, Mama celebrated her 23rd birthday crossing the Atlantic. I don't know how much longer it took her to get to shore in New York City, and I don't know if Daddy was waiting there for her or in Kansas City, but I was apparently conceived within a month of her arrival on American soil.

A new country, new state, new city, a new wife with a new husband and a new home — and now she had *morning sickness!* I was born a full-term, 8-pound 10-ounce baby less than ten months after Mama's special birthday celebration, smack dab on Daddy's 30th birthday.

Mama left her mother and sister and *cool, green England* for what she hoped would be *Prince Charming* and the *Garden of Eden.* One ocean and half a continent away, she discovered *mosquitoes* and *chiggers, sunburn* and *sweat* in the hot, humid, inhospitable Kansas summers and she was then forced to endure dark, drab, *bitterly-cold-to-the-bones* Kansas winters. Foreign diplomats received hazard pay for serving in the Midwest, the weather was that extreme.

Mama's mama lived in England and was too far away to help her daughter with her first birth.

I remember the occasional telephone call to England. Mama would call the operator here, who would make arrangements with many other operators along the way until the phone in the neighborhood phone booth in England rang. Someone passing by would answer the phone, then run and fetch Grandma.

Grandma would run to the phone booth, breathless, and the yelling would begin. Mama had to talk loudly so Grandma could hear her all the way across the Atlantic. After they were finished and the phone was back in its cradle, Mama would shake and cry.

She often clearly stated that she *hated* it in Kansas. She *hated* so many things. And *men,* she complained repeatedly, *only wanted one thing.* Yet when I asked her once why she didn't move back to England, she looked at me as if I had suggested she should live on the moon. She *hated* the United States but she had *no* desire to return to England.

The only people Mama knew in Kansas City were other English war brides, who were all brand new, inexperienced mothers… and the doctor. She didn't care to know Daddy's family. They embarrassed and offended her. She called them *hillbillies* and made them feel so unwelcome that they eventually stopped coming around.

Yet on holidays Mama shined. She always bought the perfect gifts for each person. She wrapped each gift perfectly. She made a perfect American Thanksgiving turkey dinner and a perfect roast beef or ham with broiled potatoes for Christmas. But all the rest of the days of the year, I remember her anger. It seemed she was always angry at either Daddy or me or both of us. She never laughed with us. She rarely smiled at us. Although she blessed others with beautiful smiles, she was always more than deadly serious with Daddy and me.

Mama was married for twenty-five years to Daddy and then twenty-five years to Nick. Nick taught Mama how to laugh and how to love. He brought out the best in her. When she died he was devastated. As we walked arm in arm from the parking lot to the chapel where she lay in a casket he kept saying, "You want to see something beautiful? You want to see something *really* beautiful?" He meant Mama, of course. Nick's gone now too. I wish they could have lived together forever. Together they gave me hope that love is possible.

DADDY

Daddy was a mellow fellow. He was the shy American guy who thought he'd married a British fairy princess.

Daddy smiled a lot. I suspect Mama had fallen for his easy smile. Even when he was very old, his smile still resembled my youngest photos. Daddy smiled a real smile. I remember him as a happy person... for the most part. He worshipped his wife, adored his children. He was a simple person with simple needs.

Daddy seemed to be content and capable in his capacity as an automobile mechanic. He always either smelled like gasoline and motor oil or soap and English Leather cologne.

Daddy was proud of the fact that during the war he was the only mechanic in the Army to have scored 100% on the mechanical aptitude exam. He could always fix car problems after everyone else had tried and failed. He loved figuring out what was wrong with a car, fixing it and getting it back on the road. His successes made him so happy he often forgot to charge his customers for the work he did.

Like Mama, Daddy was a perfectionist too. But he was a perfectionist only when it came to fixing cars. When it came to fixing people, he didn't... he pretty much accepted them as they were. He didn't hold a grudge. Daddy loved to read. He'd read

Webster's dictionary and World Book encyclopedias. I've since heard that other Robinetts — ones he never knew — were like that too.

My elderly cousin Winona told me about her grandpa who always carried a pocket dictionary with him. As a boy on the farm, tilling the fields, he walked behind the cow and as they turned the corner to plow a new row, he'd look in his dictionary and learn a new word.

Once when Daddy came home early he heard Mama scolding me harshly and he said, "Don't you treat my daughter like that!" That gesture of fatherly protection marked the last shred of affection between Mama and me or Mama and Daddy. From then on, she would call him, *your father,* in an especially bitter tone. When she talked to him, referring to me, she would say, *your daughter,* her voice dripping with acid.

It's understandable why he let her run the show at home and never interfered again. He dared not incur her wrath.

When I was twelve, Mama, my brothers and I spent the summer in England with Grandma. Daddy stayed home to work and pay for the trip.

As illogical as it may sound to me now, at age twelve, I felt let down by Daddy because he wasn't there in England to protect me from Mama's ire. Consequently, I was a distant daughter when I returned to Kansas that fall. I barely spoke to either parent. Daddy never knew why I had became so cold. It took me years to sort it all out.

All the surprises he had for us when we got home made Mama mad: a concrete slab called a patio, an encyclopedia, a new car. He was undoubtedly *lonely* while we were gone — the perfect target for door-to-door salesmen and we were now in *debt!* He used to like a beer at night, but while we were gone, he began to drink in earnest.

For a few years Daddy became a verbally abusive alcoholic. During those years, it was hell at home, especially at the dinner table. He would say awful things to Mike and I hated him for it. During that era, Daddy smelled like gasoline and alcohol — no English Leather.

As conditions continued to deteriorate at home, Daddy spent more and more time at work. He started coming home later and later, getting home after everyone was asleep. He started getting up earlier and earlier in the mornings, long before anyone else was awake. He said he was going fishing.

My heart was full of hatred and the death wish was nearly constant.

In the center of the empty basement floor sat a trunk of very beautiful love letters Daddy had written to Mama during the war, before they were married. As a teen, I read them and marveled at the beauty of the words. Only recently did I wonder whether Daddy had actually written them. He would sing to us from time to time and he said he'd written a song during World War II about Will Rogers, the cowboy comedian, that was sung by G.I.s all over the European theater.

Perhaps he truly was a poet and perhaps it was Mama's incessant criticism that ended the romance. Or perhaps a Cyrano de Bergerac had helped him win Mama's heart and she felt she'd been tricked.

So many questions I'd love to ask the dead.

I have a theory that Daddy had been circumcised during

the war. Doctors would line men up and circumcise soldiers one after the other, threatening them with court-martial.

Daddy always said, "The Army'll make a man outa ya!" Now that I understand about circumcision, I wonder if that is what he meant.

After Mama and Daddy divorced, Daddy married Trudy, who was just right for him. They were like two teenagers in love. They were as happy and as homely as humanly possible. She nursed him out of his alcoholism. He basked in her adoration. I have a delightful photo of the two of them smiling real smiles that always makes me giggle. Together, Daddy and Trudy gave my baby brother a warm and loving home.

BROTHERS

I had two younger brothers. As little boys, both of them were exceedingly precious and cute. Photos of them in infancy and early childhood contain eyes and smiles that were sweet, contained, strained, pained. Like most boys in those days, they had been circumcised at birth. They didn't even have a short honeymoon with their whole, intact bodies.

CUT, TWO, THREE, FOUR

CUT NUMBER ONE

She's almost one year old now and Patricia Ann Elizabeth Robinett is upstairs in the bathroom watching her Daddy shave. She is *Daddy's little girl.*

Whipping up a white, creamy lather inside a mug with a soft round brush, Daddy spreads the fluffy foam all over his cheeks, upper lip and chin: a soapy mask. He leaves a hole so he can breathe.

He begins collecting the soap on the blade, skillfully wielding the sharp razor around and about, back and forth from face to basin, dipping the blade in hot water over and over again, until all the white stuff is gone. Testing now with his fingertips to make sure his face is smooth, he's satisfied.

So he lays the razor down on the side of the sink and closes his eyes. Then he bows his head down close to the basin and splashes and rinses his face one last time.

Reaching up and taking the razor, Patricia touches it to her own lip. *Oops! Ouch!* Now there is blood.

Daddy can't see her or hear. He is busy splashing. So she turns to find Mama. Climbing backwards down the stairs as children often do, leaving a trail of red behind her, she runs to Mama for comfort and instead of a hug there is a scream.

Mama backs away.

"You're bleeding! Don't touch me! Don't get blood on my dress! What happened? What did you do? Where is your father? Robby, come and get your daughter! She's bleeding! There's blood everywhere! Robby, what on earth were you thinking? Hold still! Don't move! Don't touch me! Stay away!"

The young mother holds out a tissue to the tiny little lip. Holding the child at arm's length to keep from getting bloody, off they go to Dr. Haas' office just down the street.

"No need for stitches" he says. "A little tape will hold the skin together. Keep sharp things up high where she can't reach."

CUT NUMBER TWO

Another day. Same apartment near Daddy's work. Mama is cleaning the living room. Her tiny daughter stands watching from the sofa. Mama carefully lays a sheet of glass that protects the top of the coffee table on the arm of the soft, springy, bouncy sofa.

Ouch!

The broken glass is sharp and it hurts the little girl's foot. There is red here and red there and red almost everywhere.

Mama screams!

"Look at you! You should know better than to do that! Look what you have done! Just look at this mess! You have ruined my good sofa! What on earth could you have been thinking? What is wrong with you? Everybody knows you don't walk on glass!"

And off we go to see Dr. Haas again.

CUT NUMBER THREE

I received all the standard vaccinations and had all the standard childhood physical ailments: measles, mumps, chickenpox, colds, sore throats and ear infections. And then I had some extras: colic, the two previous cutting injuries and urinary tract infections (UTIs).

Shortly before my first birthday there was a third bloody event, a little more mysterious than the other two and this time it involved the doctor himself. This time Dr. Haas came to our house. In the 1940s and 1950s in the United States, doctors still made house calls!

The doctor visited and someone (Mama?) held me down. There was more bleeding, only this time it was between my legs and Mama didn't complain. She paid the man for his services.

Was the cutting performed by the doctor an attempt (however misguided) at controlling my urinary tract infections? Could the logic have been, *if circumcision prevents UTIs in little boys, perhaps it will help prevent UTIs in girls too?* I wonder if the doctor used that logic to carve the "extra" skin from my labia.

However, they now know that little girls have four times more UTIs than boys and most girls are treated with antibiotics. But removing skin? Removing skin rather than using antibiotics is overkill.

From my memory, this loss of my labia, although unpleasant and cruelly painful, didn't break my spirit. You saw the photos. The smiles were still open, trusting, joyful for five more years.

At this stage, I still had a clitoris, so I could still comfort myself.

CUT NUMBER FOUR

But, another genital reduction, clitoridectomy, followed a few years after the labia cutting. It appears that it was for socialization and discipline more than for health purposes. This book is primarily about that cut.

SIN & PUNISHMENT

"If only you had been a good little girl..."

What follows are things I did that girls were not supposed to do in the USA in the 1950s.

Circumcision was used by doctors and parents to punish children for *"touching themselves down there!"* and to assist girls in becoming "proper young ladies".

SIN NUMBER ONE: PLAYING DOCTOR

One warm summer day my next door neighbors Judy and Kathy (one girl was older than me and the other was younger) and I were playing *doctor* in the bushes behind their house. Their mother Edie Mae apparently saw us from a window, came out into the yard to interrupt our play and promptly reported the incident to my mother. I had committed an unforgivable sin: I had embarrassed my mother.

Looking now at the photos of Edie Mae's daughters, I have to admit that in all of the photos I have of the two sisters they look joyless, much like my "post-circumcision" photos. I wonder now if the doctor had cut them as well. I wonder if my mother got the idea for my circumcision from Edie Mae.

Our *playing doctor* in the bushes was quite innocent. I think we simply took turns being patients and doctors, lying down on the ground and using sticks as if they were rectal thermometers. It was quite thrilling to feel my bare buttocks exposed to the open air and to be touched in hidden parts of my body! I had no concept of sex or erotica. It just felt good to be touched and to be outdoors.

And why was it that as children we already felt a need to hide in the bushes to *play doctor*? How did we know that we were supposed to hide and feel guilty? How did we know it was "bad" to be naked, to touch and be touched, to be doing doctor things?

Why is the game of *playing doctor* so widespread? How is it that children all over the country *play doctor*? Do they play it all over the world? Do children who have natural births *play doctor*? Why is *playing doctor* so threatening to adults?

Is *playing doctor* the ingenious, naughty invention of tiny children? Or are they merely imitating what they have experienced in medical situations with real doctors?

Why are children dramatizing what has happened to them in hospitals and doctors offices? And why is *playing doctor* a punishable offense?

This is what *acting out* is: *acting out* is using actions to express what you cannot say in words. *Acting out* is telling stories with our actions. "This happened to me!"

We love others as we were loved. We treat others as we were treated. We punish others as we were punished.

Nothing is irrational when all the facts are known.

For instance, the myth of Dracula was based on Vlad the

Impaler, the son of the prince of Wallachia. Vlad and his brother who were held hostage by a Turkish sultan to discourage his father from invading Turkey. In captivity, Vlad was circumcised as was the custom in Turkey and then was trained to become a *janissary*, a member of the elite guard that protected the sultan.

When European Christians led by the *White Knight* invaded Turkey, Vlad and his brother were beaten daily and imprisoned where they could witness beatings, mutilations, torture and executions in the courtyard outside the window of their cell.

When Vlad's father and brother were murdered by the defeated, retreating Christian army, Vlad managed to escape Turkey and return to Wallachia to claim the throne. He eventually killed tens of thousands of men, women and children, inflicting the extreme tortures he had learned from his captors. He acted out, dramatized, his own experience.

Not every person who has been tortured will become a torturer. One person might avoid human contact altogether while another might pass on the abuse.

It is impossible to know how a specific person will react to cruel treatment but it seems safe to conjecture that few natural people who were raised with love and respect would spontaneously invent torture in a vacuum. Very few would ever think to put a sharp knife to infant genitals. Those who do have been taught by example, usually because it happened to them. Victims of trauma pass on the trauma by acting out their unresolved distress.

Some adults become doctors and act out or *play doctor* for a profit. They clamp babies' heads and pull them or cut them out of their mothers' wombs. They put implements into children's ears, eyes, noses, rectums, vaginas, stab them with needles, restrain them against their will, and mutilate their genitals — as it was done to them.

Are these people intentionally cruel? Or are they merely unconscious puppets in a long abusive game of monkey-see, monkey-do, pass-it-down, do unto others before they do it to you? Was *Jack the Ripper* a product of this phenomenon?

SIN NUMBER TWO: HIDE & SEEK & THE BATHROOM

One day when I was in kindergarten or first grade, some nice people came to visit — a woman and her son. I don't remember much more other than the two mothers sat at the kitchen table while we children played *hide and seek*.

Mike, my brother, was *it*. The little boy and I hid in the bathroom which was adjacent to the kitchen where our mothers were chatting. The bathtub was located against the back wall with a window above that looked out over the backyard.

If we stood on tiptoe on the edge of the tub then we could peek out the window and spy on Mike. He ran all over the yard trying to find us, but we knew he would never look for us in the bathroom. Bursting to giggle, we tried to be very, very quiet.

At some point during the game I used the toilet. Mama had taught me that it was not OK to let little boys see me with my pants down, so in the same way that I had learned to hide behind a towel when changing from bathing suit to street clothes on the beach in England, I took a small rug from the floor, sat down on the toilet and modestly covered my lap.

Standing on the edge of the tub, the little boy whispered a running commentary, telling me where Mike was, as he searched for us in the sand pile, the mulberry bush and the side yard.

I finished, quietly closed the toilet lid and placed the rug back down on the floor. I didn't flush, because I thought the noise might alert my brother to our hiding place.

When Mike gave up and called, "Ally ally in free! Come out, come out wherever you are!" the little boy and I triumphantly ran out of the bathroom. Then I remembered that I hadn't flushed so I ran back into the bathroom and flushed the toilet.

Most other mothers would surely have smiled at our antics but when it came to me, Mama had no sense of humor. She exploded right there in front of our company.

"Patricia Ann Elizabeth Robinett! Shame on you! You used the toilet with a little boy in the bathroom?"

I began to whine an excuse. "I didn't let him see me! I put a rug over my lap!"

Nevertheless, she took charge of her wild-animal daughter and did the right thing for animal trainers to do. She spanked me right there in front of our company. I had committed two unforgivable sins in her eyes: I'd used the toilet with a little boy in the room and I'd embarrassed her in front of company.

Those nice people never came back to visit.

SIN NUMBER THREE: MY KINDERGARTEN SWEETHEART

The children in my kindergarten class were building cardboard houses and stores for a make-believe town while Dudley and I strolled around the classroom hand in hand, overseeing the construction.

Affection. Companionship. Holding hands. It was all quite pure, of course but it might have concerned the teacher Miss

Gibson, or our mothers. So many innocent sins.

SIN NUMBER FOUR: PUSHING A BOY

Then there was the time I pushed a little boy out of line in the first grade for crowding in front of me: more unladylike behavior.

I was sent to Miss Kenton's office. The principal of Chelsea Grade School was a tall, thin spinster who lived in the big house on the hill. I passed that house when I had extra time and walked the long, scenic route to school. I believe it was Miss Kenton's job to make sure all the little girls grew up to be proper young ladies. Perhaps she had made the suggestion to my mother.

SIN NUMBER FIVE: TOUCHING MYSELF

I will never forget Mama's way of screaming at the top of her lungs, as if I had killed somebody: *Don't touch yourself!*

I knew something was wrong, but I wasn't exactly sure what it was. And she didn't say what was wrong. *Don't touch yourself!* was all she said. No explanation. No information. Just a loud, shrill *Don't touch yourself!*

Mama always had trouble talking about important things. It wasn't her way. She had friends she complained to, gossiped with, laughed with — friends whose children also had that troubled, less than happy demeanor — could it be that all of them had tamed their daughters with the scalpel?

With her family, especially when we children were little, Mama would tease or nag, scream or yell, huff and puff... so we knew something was wrong. We knew she was upset, but she would never come right out and say what was bothering her. She was an enigma to all of us. She was a "read-my-mind" kind of woman.

So, *Don't touch yourself!* was probably as close as she could get to addressing the subject of masturbation.

I wonder how different my life would have been if she had simply sat down with me, looked me in the eyes, held my hands and said kindly and gently, "Honey, please don't touch yourself between your legs when other people are around. It's not appropriate to do that in public. It embarrasses me and people might think I'm a bad mother."

I suspect I might have understood and responded if she had made it simple and clear.

But no, that was not her way.

So when hinting and suggesting, pouting, storming and yelling and hitting didn't work, I guess that's when she turned to the doctor. She could talk to the doctor about things she could not, or would not, say to anyone else.

Was he the one who posed the solution — a *circumcision!*

I'm fairly sure he must have called it *circumcision,* because that word was stuck in my mind and — remember? — blinking in neon.

Was that doctor a uniquely dirty old man? Not really. Doctors in the U.S. recommended clitoridectomies well into the 1970s, as a cure for children who touched themselves.

In his Christian coming-of-age manual, *On Becoming a Woman: A book for teenage girls,* Dr. Harold Shryock wrote:

> There are teenage girls who, impelled by an unwholesome curiosity or by the example of unscrupulous girl friends, have

fallen into the habit of manipulating these sensitive tissues as a means of excitement. This habit is spoken of as masturbation... There is an anatomical factor that sometimes causes irritation about the clitoris and thus encourages a manipulation of the delicate reproductive organs... Oftentimes the remedy for this situation consists of a minor surgical operation spoken of as circumcision. This operation is not hazardous and is much to be preferred to allowing the condition of irritation to continue.

Written in 1951, Shryock's book could have easily been a factor in my mother's decision to have me circumcised.

Interestingly, I encountered Shryock's grandson on an Internet discussion group. He expressed confidence to the people discussing female circumcision that his grandfather would have never suggested such a thing... I encouraged him to read his grandfather's book.

THEY REALLY GOT ME THIS TIME, KATHY

Working as a regression therapist through the years, I became aware that no memory is ever lost, just temporarily forgotten. I wanted to know more about the clitoridectomy and I knew it was all stored in my mind's filing cabinet. However, to approach a memory of someone taking a scalpel to my genitals was too scary for me to do all by myself, especially after reading what doctors had written about circumcision:

Dr. John Harvey Kellogg — yes, of *Kellogg's Corn Flakes* and *Raisin Bran* fame — wrote quite explicitly in his 1877 book *Plain Facts for Old and Young: Embracing the natural history and hygiene of organic life*:

> The operation should be performed by a surgeon without administering an anesthetic, as the brief pain attending the operation will have a salutary effect upon the mind, especially if it be connected with the idea of punishment, as it may well be in some cases. The soreness which continues for several weeks interrupts the practice, and if it had not previously become too firmly fixed, it may be forgotten and not resumed.
>
> In females, the author has found the application of pure carbolic acid to the clitoris an excellent means of allaying the

abnormal excitement, and preventing the recurrence of the practice in those whose willpower has become so weakened that the patient is unable to exercise entire self-control.

A doctor, ironically named "Angel Money", wrote the following in his 1887 book *Treatment of Disease in Children:*

> There can be no doubt of [masturbation's] injurious effect, and of the proneness to practice it on the part of children with defective brains. Circumcision should always be practiced. It may be necessary to make the genitals so sore by blistering fluids that pain results from attempts to rub the parts.

These words are not the words of an angel. What drives adult men and women to target little children's genitals for mutilation? Their own damage, passing on the abuse they received when they were children.

Dr. Angel Money also advocated leeching and opium, *morphia,* strychnia, arsenic and belladonna. Was his goal to heal or to punish? In either case, there certainly seemed to be a blurring of the line between science and religious morality.

Convinced that only the kindest healer would be able to help me R-E-M-E-M-B-E-R and release the fear around my circumcision, it took several years for me to find the right person.

When Kathy and Tom moved to town, I was sure these two really were genuine angels sent straight from heaven specifically for me. Gentle Kathy was someone I felt I could trust. When we started working together, things began to slowly move. Even then, it was months before I could relax enough to approach the clitoridectomy issue.

A little bit of memory here, a little bit there, and finally we struck a vein. Choking on my tears, I involuntarily said over and over, *They really got me this time, Kathy. They really got me. They got me real good.* We had found the little girl.

I realized that around age seven was the second time I had been circumcised — once at age one year and again when I was in school.

Before, I could touch my good-feeling place, my clitoris, and feel better — no matter how mad Mama was. The good feelings soothed me and made the bad feelings go away. That is why my early portraits were consistently joyous.

But with the second circumcision, the clitoridectomy, my source of comfort was gone. After the surgery, touching myself made me only feel worse, not better. There were crusty scabs and excruciating pain. It was painful every time I went to the bathroom. Painful every time I moved. Painful every time Mama cleaned the wound.

All I could do was to curl up in my bed and cry. I wanted to be dead. This was surely the surgery that Mama referred to when she said, *You never were the same after your surgery.* Yes, this was a life-changing event. And it surely was the inspiration for my attempt to find a knife to cut out my heart.

There were no more good feelings. There was no more comfort. No more soothing. No more buffer from life. Just jangled, jumbled, jammed up feelings between my legs and an angry Mama who thought she needed to tame her daughter. Yes, indeed, *They really got me this time, Kathy.*

They hurt my body, but even worse they broke my spirit, my will to live and my ability to trust and love. I was not tamed — I was broken.

I wish Mama and I could have talked before the doctor took out his knife. If she had asked me, maybe I could have explained to her how very innocent I was and how very innocent was my touching. I had no idea how sex worked until I was an eighteen-year-old in college and met the boy I married.

Self-touching had been a source of solace, a way for me to stay sane in the absence of affection. People die without touch, you know. The English are not known for their warmth and affection. Daddy was at work most of the time. The only touch in our home was harsh, used for control, correction and punishment: forcing me in a particular direction, at a certain speed, yanking me along, spanking — always harsh. No softness nor tenderness, no affection or sweetness.

The admonishment *Don't touch yourself!* really stuck. Throughout my entire life I took brief showers, going to great lengths to obey that ancient dictum. I feared touching myself *anywhere*. It never occurred to me that she was referring to a specific area when she said *Don't touch yourself!*

The clitoridectomy was the origin of my death wish. I lost more than body parts; I lost trust. I felt betrayed. I lost my faith in humans and in the goodness of life.

I could not let anyone close to me. No one. The parents took care of my food, clothing and shelter but I could not share my happiness with them or ask them for time or care. I no longer felt safe.

I felt *very* alone, *very* afraid and *very* angry. I had to take care of myself now — I could trust no one else to protect me. I was tense all day, every day. If my own family could not be trusted then I had to be on guard even at home in my bed. I could never let my defenses down.

Alone in the world. Afraid for my very life. And I was only seven years old. I was astonished when I made it to age 12; I never thought I would live that long.

We live in a world of men who have been through this. It finally made sense to me, and answered my question, *Why are men the way they are?*

A HAPPY SHIFT

My birthday falls at the end of the busy winter holiday sea-
son. After Thanksgiving, Christmas and New Year, most people
are tired of gifts, parties, cookies and cakes, so I often celebrate
my birthday by myself, in peace and quiet.

On the evening of my 47th birthday, as I sat on the floor in
my office, resting and reading, the telephone rang. On the other
end of the line was Mama's voice.

"Happy birthday, Treesh!" she said.

Oh, dear, thought I. *Trapped.*

She was quite courageous to have called. One sunny day
in May, I had gone to the store to find a Mother's Day card and
could not find one I felt comfortable sending to her so I left the
store empty-handed.

I honestly admitted to myself that I had no interest in hearing her criticisms of me and my life choices. I didn't trust her
enough to share my heart. And as far as I was concerned, there
was no need to continue a charade. Clear at last about my feelings, I refused to speak to her for two and a half years.

So after I thanked her for giving birth to me, the conversation disintegrated. Soon I realized how wise the decision had

been to not talk to her.

She hadn't changed. Mama was still the critical parent, the correcting mother. She still saw me as no more than an extension of herself. Even as an adult I was to be *seen but not heard.* She really didn't know me or like me as a person in my own right.

Mama wanted me to marry and have children — not for my sake, but for hers. She seemed to be the turning point in my romances. For instance, when she and I, Nick, Mike's family and my new boyfriend were at a restaurant, she asked us, "When are you two going to get married and have children so I can take photos of my grandchildren to work and show them to my friends?"

My boyfriend sank into his chair and quickly disappeared once dinner ended, never to be seen again.

So on the evening of my 47th birthday, the conversation slid rapidly downhill. I was sick at heart to hear the same barrage of criticism and attempts to make me feel guilty, the same manipulative words she had spoken so many times before.

Mama honestly didn't know how to talk to me in any other way than she always had. She was a piano with only one key and so she could play only one note.

After 47 years of seeing me as a *child,* as an underling who should serve her needs, perform properly or be punished, she had no concept of seeing me as an adult worthy of love and respect.

Then I realized that I had judgments and expectations of her too and if I waited for her to become the wise and loving mother I wanted her to be, I might have to wait forever.

If anything was going to change, I would have to make it

happen. I would have to become the leader, because I had by then acquired a few tools that could help change the dynamic between us.

Closing my eyes in exasperation, I asked for a miracle, a shift in perception.

I am willing, I said silently, *to see this differently.*

Immediately after I thought it, a few simple, honest and sincere words jumped out of my mouth without going first through my mind…

"I just want us to love each other and to be friends."

I was shocked. It was obvious that Mama was shocked too. We were both speechless. Neither of us had ever said anything like that to each other before. A few pristine silent moments passed. When the conversation began again, it was civil for a few minutes. My heart fell when it returned to discord.

So I repeated to myself *I am willing to see this differently.*

Interestingly, the same words came out again…

"I just want us to love each other and to be friends."

We stopped cold for a few moments and then our conversation became loving and respectful for another few minutes.

We repeated this back and forth pattern three or four times until something old and rigid gave way and the entire quality of our relationship shifted forever. Our mother-daughter roles miraculously fell away. The old, competitive, adversarial relationship shifted to a sparkling new, loving and respectful friendship. *A Course in Miracles* says,

> *The holiest of all the spots on earth is where an ancient hatred has become a present love.*

For the next three years our interactions, by phone and in person, continued to be patient and kind and caring. Then, Mama my friend, died peacefully in the arms of her loving husband Nick.

MOTHER & CHILD LIBERATION

I had intended to end this book at this point. After all, I had already covered my discovery of female genital mutilation in the USA, my understanding of circumcision of baby boys, and I mentioned the cutting of mothers during labor. I was done — or so I thought.

But then I heard about something called "pit to distress", the intentional overdosing of women in labor on *pitocin* (the induction drug) to speed contractions, resulting in an iatrogenically caused emergency situation, so that a doctor can justify a cesarean section, major surgery, which is far more profitable than a simple, gentle, natural birth where nature does the work for free.

I shook my head, clenched my jaw, closed my eyes, covered my mouth, and screamed "No!" into my hands.

The cutting of mothers affects nearly all of us, for only a fortunate few in America have been birthed naturally, without shock and trauma.

Then, the final straw. I saw a photo of a newborn baby boy whose face looked as if he had been thoroughly tortured, and then tortured again. I have never seen such an angry face on a tiny baby. If looks could kill...

Something in my gut said he had been through the pit of hell via both "pit to distress" and circumcision. I returned to the keyboard. I wrote a lot but decided to put it all in another book that will be released later.

Why? Because an emergency arose.

In 1996, when the FGM Bill was enacted, genital cutting in America did not end. Girls were protected, but boys were not. Special clauses in the FGM bill allowed doctors to cut women as they saw fit. Obstetricians are trained as surgeons and cutting is what surgeons do. "Have knife, will cut." Consequently, the cutting of women has dramatically increased since 1996. Episiotomies are fewer only because Cesarean sections are on the rise.

And at this time (May 2010), the American Academy of Pediatrics (AAP) wants to claim a right to cut baby girls' genitals. They have issued a new policy statement proposing changes to the 1996 Female Genital Mutilation (FGM) Act.

The AAP wants to change the law to allow pediatricians to perform a "ritual nick" of girls' genitals, so families whose cultures accept FGM don't send their daughters overseas for the full genital cutting procedure.

The same system that birthed and circumcised me and my brothers, the same system that put my mother in shock ("They cut me!") for the last 50 of her years on planet earth — that same abusive system has not died out. It wants more.

I wish I could say this book is merely an account of an historical abuse in the past, but I cannot. Women and children are still threatened by medical personnel and the momentum seems to be growing rather than diminishing. Cesarean sections are at an all-time high of 33%.

Rather than help mothers relax, go with nature and have ecstatic births, hospital boards demand doctors perform cesarean sections — to protect not the health of mother and child, but to protect doctor and hospital from lawsuits.

Merely showing up at a hospital signals medical personnel to pull out their big guns. Mother is immediately put on a conveyer belt. She is hooked up to an IV "just in case" she needs an emergency intervention. And then the birth is forced to progress on to a timetable that is set by "experts" — not by nature, the mother or child. Pit to distress makes birth a risky business.

Nature is not foolish. If an animal in labor is in danger, the fetus is pulled securely back into the body so the animal can make a hasty escape. When she is safe and can relax again, the birth proceeds.

Hospital attitudes and assumptions frighten mothers to the point where they contract in fear and labor halts. Then medical personnel begin to force the birth.

Nature is not allowed to work in its own time, for consultants have determined that hospital beds should be emptied as quickly as possible for the sake of the hospital's bottom line. Medicine is, after all, a business.

Due to this overly enthusiastic (expensive) medical system, far too many mothers are cut, then they wearily drag themselves home with their drugged, bruised, oxygen- and blood-deprived babies.

Where is the joy? Watch *Birth As We Know It*. You will see joy is in birthing. Nature knows best. Not a gang of masked strangers wielding knives in a cold, sterile operating theater.

A huge percentage of hospital births result in postpartum depression because mothers have been overpowered and feel railroaded into excessive, intrusive medical care that they did not choose, did not want, did not anticipate. Their carefully crafted birth plans are discarded in the circular file cabinet.

When a traumatized mother looks at her child, she remembers not the first moment their eyes met, but she remembers, "They cut me".

When a baby looks at the mother with a mixture of shock and betrayal, he is thinking, "Why didn't you protect me from those bad people? Where were you when they hurt me?"

Where is the love?

Love and fear are opposites. Trauma precludes love.

FBI researchers say that *violence begets violence.* Children born in hospitals are born screaming. The males who are held down and cut on their genitals, scream until they are unconscious. The safety and happiness of the world are at stake as long as mothers associate birth with violence, and male children associate the circumcision betrayal with mothers.

As long as cutting and cruelty are all the rage, both rage and cruelty will be passed down from generation to generation. Is it a coincidence that the only three cultures that circumcise their young are today, in 2010, at war in the Middle East?

Hatred, anger, fury, anyone? Misogyny?

Where is the peace? Native Americans of the Hopi tribe protected their infants from external disturbances and allowed them to luxuriate in the peace within. Our birthing methods yank the child out of its nest and throw it into fear and terror.

It appears it may be the responsibility of laypersons to end the medical abuse of mothers and children.

Many may not know — I didn't — that midwife-assisted deliveries are 19% lower in morbidity and mortality than physician-assisted deliveries. It is not birth itself that is dangerous, but the intrusive practices the medical field has developed.

There is no need for induction and cutting of nearly every mother. There is no need for the genital mutilation of children.

There is no need to send mothers to hospitals, which are rife with germs of every description, where — believe it or not — some doctors still don't wash their hands. *Hundreds of people die needlessly every day in the US*, due to this simple lack of hygiene.

> Hand-washing failures contribute to infections linked to health care that kill almost 100,000 Americans a year and cost U.S. hospitals $4 billion to $29 billion a year to combat, said Dr. Mark Chassin, who leads the Joint Commission, which sets standards and accredits hospitals and health care organizations.
>
> Chassin's announcement came after Hearst Newspapers published the results of an investigation, "Dead by Mistake," which reported that 247 people die every day in the United States from infections contracted in hospitals.

This article written by Carolyn Lochhead was published in the San Francisco Chronicle on September 11, 2009, exactly eight years after 2,752 people died in one of the greatest tragedies in our nation's history. Yet 247 people die *every day* — *2,752 every 11 days and 90,155 every year* — due to infections contracted in American hospitals. That's the equivalent of more than two World Trade Center disasters monthly and nearly 33 each year.

God bless us and protect us, every one, from our very own medical professionals, for they are killing far more Americans every month than terrorists ever have!

Doctors and nurses contribute to deaths caused by preventable hospital infections because they washed their hands only 50 percent of the time that they enter or exit a patient's room. In some cases, the problems were logistical and easy to fix. In other cases, there was *"an attitude of impunity, arrogance* and *lack of concern about patients"*.

"Certainly there are some individuals who believe they are above the law," Joint Commission President Mark Chassin said, "and their peers and others are reluctant to call their omissions to their attention."

There is a need for clean, peaceful environments; reassuring, experienced help (only mothers and *very* compassionate males need apply), and protection from drugs and knives.

We vote with our dollars. Americans are turning away from the knife-happy, drug-pushing, fear-mongering, bullying, disrespectful medical arena, toward alternative means of healing and birthing, where they find kind, respectful, humble practitioners, safety and efficacy.

Please inform yourself, your family and friends. If we can't turn this unwieldy medical steamroller around, perhaps it's time to send the American medical clunker — 37th in the world in health — to the junk yard.

MY PRAYER

A few years ago, when I learned about my circumcision and began to focus on releasing the fear, my night terrors and death wish finally ended. I realized I could feel as good here, in this moment, as anytime, anywhere, past or future. So I decided to enjoy the rest of my time in this body and to do what I could to improve the quality of life on planet earth.

As a clinical hypnotherapist, I have spent many long hours de-hypnotizing clients from past trauma so they could live happy, healthy, productive lives. But picking up the pieces after the damage is done is a slow way to effect change. It is far more efficient to prevent abuse in the first place.

I know it is possible for everyone to be welcomed to the planet with love, honor, dignity and respect.

I know it is possible for us all to be safe from harm.

I know there will come a time when sharp knives will be used only and ever to cut vegetables and never to cut people for reasons of fear, superstition, social conformity, or financial profit.

I know that someday in the future, historians will be aghast to discover that at one point in the history of the world, children's genitals were cut. *How primitive,* they will think.

I know it is possible for us all to live outside the shadow of fear.

Please do what you can to help. Seeing the world aright and learning to set limits without offense, *Thank you but no thank you... I don't feel comfortable with that...* are some of the most powerful things you can do.

Thank you for reading this book. Please share it, pass it on, give it to others as gifts. Ask libraries and bookstores to stock it. Ask radio and television hosts to discuss the topic. Write compassionately yet boldly on Internet forums. Point out the inevitable logical fallacies in any argument for cutting genitals.

And ask important questions. "How would you feel if you were strapped down and cut in that way?"

If honest, no adult who supports infant circumcision would allow it to be done to them, unless there is perhaps a propensity in them toward masochism.

Speak out with love. There is no need to apologize for protecting the human rights of babies.

They shall not hurt nor destroy
in all my holy mountain:
for the earth shall be full
of the Knowledge of the Lord,
as the waters cover the sea.
Isaiah 11:9

REFERENCES . RESOURCES

THE FGM BILL

September 30, 1996.
104th Congress, 2nd Session
HR 4278 RDS

SEC. 644. INFORMATION REGARDING FEMALE GENITAL MUTILATION.

(a) PROVISION OF INFORMATION REGARDING FEMALE GENITAL MUTILATION.—The Immigration and Naturalization Service (in cooperation with the Department of State) shall make available for all aliens who are issued immigrant or nonimmigrant visas, prior to or at the time of entry into the United States, the following information:

(1) Information on the severe harm to physical and psychological health caused by female genital mutilation which is compiled and presented in a manner which is limited to the practice itself and respectful to the cultural values of the societies in which such practice takes place.

(2) Information concerning potential legal consequences in the United States for (A) performing female genital mutilation, or (B) allowing a child under his or her care to be subjected to female genital mutilation, under criminal or child protection statutes or as a form of child abuse.

(b) LIMITATION.—In consultation with the Secretary of State, the Commissioner of Immigration and Naturalization shall identify those countries in which female genital mutilation is commonly practiced and, to the extent practicable, limit the provision of information under subsection (a) to aliens from such countries.

(c) DEFINITION.—For purposes of this section, the term "female genital mutilation" means the removal or infibulation (or both) of the whole or part of the clitoris, the labia minora, or labia majora.

SEC. 645. CRIMINALIZATION OF FEMALE GENITAL MUTILATION.

(a) FINDINGS.—The Congress finds that—

(1) the practice of female genital mutilation is carried out by members of certain cultural and religious groups within the United States;

(2) the practice of female genital mutilation often results in the occurrence of physical and psychological health effects that harm the women involved;

(3) such mutilation infringes upon the guarantees of rights secured by Federal and State law, both statutory and constitutional;

(4) the unique circumstances surrounding the practice of female genital mutilation place it beyond the ability of any single State or local jurisdiction to control;

(5) the practice of female genital mutilation can be prohibited without abridging the exercise of any rights guaranteed under the first amendment to the Constitution or under any other law; and

(6) Congress has the affirmative power under section 8 of article I, the necessary and proper clause, section 5 of the fourteenth amendment, as well as under the treaty clause, to the Constitution to enact such legislation.

(b) CRIME.—

(1) IN GENERAL.—Chapter 7 of title 18, United States Code, is amended by adding at the end the following:

"§116. Female genital mutilation

"(a) Except as provided in subsection (b), whoever knowingly circumcises, excises, or infibulates the whole or any part of the labia majora or labia minora or clitoris of another person who has not attained the age of 18 years shall be fined under this title or imprisoned not more than 5 years, or both.

"(b) A surgical operation is not a violation of this section if the operation is—

"(1) necessary to the health of the person on whom it is performed, and is performed by a person licensed in the place of its performance as a medical practitioner; or

"(2) performed on a person in labor or who has just given birth and is performed for medical purposes connected with that labor or birth by a person licensed in the place it is performed as a medical practitioner, midwife, or person in training to become such a practitioner or midwife.

"(c) In applying subsection (b)(1), no account shall be taken of the effect on the person on whom the operation is to be performed of any belief on the part of that person, or any other person, that the operation is required as a matter of custom or ritual.".

(2) CONFORMING AMENDMENT.—The table of sections at the beginning of chapter 7 of title 18, United States Code, is amended by adding at the end the following new item:

"§116. Female genital mutilation."

(c) EFFECTIVE DATE.—The amendments made by subsection (b) shall take effect on the date that is 180 days after the date of the enactment of this Act.

NO NATIONAL MEDICAL ORGANIZATION IN THE WORLD RECOMMENDS CIRCUMCISION

2003 BRITISH MEDICAL ASSOCIATION

The BMA does not believe that parental preference alone constitutes sufficient grounds for performing a surgical procedure on a child unable to express his own view... Parental preference must be weighed in terms of the child's interests... The BMA considers that the evidence concerning health benefit from non-therapeutic circumcision is insufficient for this alone to be a justification for doing it... Some doctors may wish to not perform circumcisions for reasons of conscience. Doctors are under no obligation to comply with a request to circumcise a child.

2002 ROYAL AUSTRALASIAN COLLEGE OF PHYSICIANS

After extensive review of the literature the RACP reaffirms that there is no medical indication for routine male circumcision. The possibility that routine circumcision may contravene human rights has been raised because circumcision is performed on a minor and is without proven medical benefit... Review of the literature in relation to risks and benefits shows there is no evidence of benefit outweighing harm for circumcision as a routine procedure.

2002 CANADIAN PAEDIATRIC SOCIETY

Circumcision of newborns should not be routinely performed. (Reaffirmed its 1996 position.)

2000 AMERICAN MEDICAL ASSOCIATION

The AMA supports the general principles of the 1999 Circumcision Policy Statement of the American Academy of Pediatrics.

1999 AMERICAN ACADEMY OF PEDIATRICS

Existing scientific evidence demonstrates potential medical benefits of newborn male circumcision; however, these data are not sufficient to recommend routine neonatal circumcision.

1996 AUSTRALIAN COLLEGE OF PAEDIATRICS

The Australasian Association of Paediatric Surgeons has informed the College that "neonatal male circumcision has no medical indication. It is a traumatic procedure performed without anaesthesia to remove a normal functional and protective prepuce."

1996 AUSTRALASIAN ASSOCIATION
OF PAEDIATRIC SURGEONS

We do not support the removal of a normal part of the body, unless there are definite indications to justify the complications and risks which may arise. In particular, we are opposed to male children being subjected to a procedure, which had they been old enough to consider the advantages and disadvantages, may well have opted to reject the operation and retain their prepuce... The 1989 United Nations Convention on the Rights of the Child states that "State parties should take all effective and appropriate measures with a view to abolishing traditional practices prejudicial to the health of children."

IN SHORT...

No national medical organization in the world recommends routine male infant circumcision

READING & VIEWING

BOOKS

Alice Miller
For Your Own Good : Hidden Cruelty in Child-Rearing and the Roots of Violence (1983)
Thou Shalt Not Be Aware: Society's Betrayal of the Child (1984)
Banished Knowledge : Facing Childhood Injuries (1990)
Breaking Down the Wall of Silence : The Liberating Experience of Facing Painful Truth (1997)
The Truth Will Set You Free: Overcoming Emotional Blindness (2001)
The Body Never Lies : The Lingering Effects of Cruel Parenting (2005)

Ann Dally
Women under the Knife (1991)

Ann Wilson Schaef
When Society Becomes an Addict (1987)

Ashley Montagu
Touching : The Human Significance of Skin (1971)

Barbara Harper & Suzanne Arms
Gentle Birth Choices (2005)

David Chamberlain
The Mind of Your Newborn Baby (1998)

David Gollaher
Circumcision : A History of the World's Most Controversial Surgery (2001)

Frederick Leboyer
Birth without Violence (1976)

George Orwell
Nineteen Eighty-Four (1948)

George Ryley Scott
Phallic Worship: A History of Sex and Sexual Rites (1995)

Guy Adams & Danny Balfour
Unmasking Administrative Evil, (2004)

Hanny Lightfoot-Klein
Prisoners of Ritual : Female Genital Mutilation in Africa (1989), Children's Genitals under the Knife (2008)
A Woman's Odyssey into Africa: Tracks across a life (2008)

Jed Diamond
The Warrior's Journey Home: Healing Men, Healing the Planet (1994)
The Irritable Male Syndrome (2004)

Jennifer Freyd
Betrayal Trauma : The Logic of Forgetting Childhood Abuse (1996)

Jim Bigelow
The Joy of Uncircumcising (1994) — Purchase pdf at norm.org/joy.html

John Colapinto
As Nature Made Him: The Boy Who was Raised as a Girl (2006)

Joseph Chilton Pearce
Magical Child (1992)
The Biology of Transcendence (2002)

Kristen and Jeffrey O'Hara
Sex As Nature Intended It (2002) & www.SexAsNatureIntendedIt.com

Leonard Glick
Marked in Your Flesh (2005)

Lillian Rubin
The Transcendent Child : Tales of Triumph over the Past (1996)

Lisa Bisque
You Call This Love? The Real Reason Women Don't Like Sex (2000)

Lloyd Demause
Foundations of Psychohistory (1982)

Michael Greger, MD
Heart Failure: Diary of a Third Year Medical Student (2000)

Paul Fleiss and Frederick Hodges
What Your Doctor May Not Tell You about Circumcision (2002)

Robert Darby
A Surgical Temptation : The Demonization of the Foreskin and the Rise of Circumcision in Britain (2005)

Robert Jay Lifton
Nazi Doctors: Medical Killing and the Psychology of Genocide (1986)

Robert Mendelsohn
Confessions of a Medical Heretic (1979)
MalePractice (1981)
How to Raise a Healthy Child in Spite of Your Doctor (1987)

Robert K. Miller
Collection of Tears: Tales of Sexual Abuse Told through the Eyes of a Little Boy (2008)

Robin Karr-Morse and Meredith Wiley
Ghosts from the Nursery : Tracing the Roots of Violence (1997)

Ron Goldman
Circumcision, The Hidden Trauma : How an American Cultural Practice, Affects Infants and Ultimately Us All (1997)
Questioning Circumcision: A Jewish Perspective (1997)

Rosemary Romberg
Circumcision: The Painful Dilemma (1985) or you can read excerpts on the web at www.peacefulbeginnings.org

Sheldon Rampton and John Stauber Romberg
Trust Us, We're Experts: How Industry Manipulates Science and Gambles

with Your Future (2002)
Toxic Sludge is Good for You — Lies, Damn Lies and the Public Relations Industry (2002)

Thomas R. Golden
Swallowed by a Snake: The gift of the masculine side of healing (2000)

CD-ROM

Denis Postle
Letting the Heart Sing - The Mind Gymnasium (CDROM 2003)

MAGAZINES

Journal of Psychohistory
(Special issue: The Sexual Abuse of Children, Vol. 19, No. 2, Fall 1991)

Mothering Magazine

Midwifery Today

MAGAZINE & JOURNAL ARTICLES
(See also Circumcision Information & Resource Pages at www.cirp.org)

"The Ritual of Circumcision," by Paige, *Human Nature,* May (1978)

"The Effects of Circumcision on Sleep-Wake States in Human Neonates," by Anders and Chalemian in *Psychosomatic Medicine* (1974)

"Continuous Stimulation and Arousal Level in Infancy: Effects of Stimulus Intensity and Stress," by Brackbill in *Child Development* (1975)

"Acetaminophen Analgesis in Neonatal Circumcision: The Effect on Pain," by Howard, Howard and Weitzman in *Pediatrics* (1994)

"Circumcision: II. Effects upon Mother-Infant Interaction," by Marshall et al. in *Early Human Development* (1982)

"Behavioral Effects of Circumcision with and without Anesthesia," by Dixon in *Journal of Development and Behavioral Pediatrics* (1984)

"Infant Responses During and Following Circumcision" by Ron Goldman at *www.circumcision.org*/response.htm

"Male circumcision: pain, trauma and psychosexual sequelae" by Boyle, Goldman, Svoboda and Fernandez in *J Health Psychology* (2002)

"The Undertreatment of Pain in Children: An Overview" by Schechter in *"Pediatric Clinics of North America* (1989)

"The Use of Lidocaine-Prilocaine Cream for Vaccination Pain in Infants" by Taddio et al., in *Journal of Pediatrics* (1994) and "Effect of Neonatal Circumcision on Pain Responses during Vaccination of Boys" in *The Lancet* (1995)

"Circumcision: I. Effects upon Newborn Behavior" by Marshall et al. in *Infant Behavior and Development* (1980)

"Pain and Its Effects in the Human Neonate and Fetus" by Anand and Hickey in *New England Journal of Medicine* (1987)

"Incidence rate of first-time symptomatic urinary tract infection in children under 6 years of age" by Mårild and Jodal in *Acta Paediatr* (1998)

MOVIES

Barbara Harper
Gentle Birth Choices (1994)

Danae Elon
Partly Private (2009), Winner: Best New York Documentary (Ms. Elon is also the 2009 recipient in the Film category of the John Simon Guggenheim Memorial Foundation Fellowship to Assist Research and Artistic Creation

Debby Takikawa
What Babies Want (2004)

Debra Pascali-Bonaro,
Orgasmic Birth

Elena Tonetti
Birth as We Know It (2006)

Frederick Leboyer
Birth without Violence (2008)

L. Janel Martin
The Other Side of the Glass (2009)
We Can Be Much Kinder (2009)
His Moment of Awe (2009)

Steve Buonagurio
Pregnant in America

ORGANIZATIONS

At the time of this printing, there are no organizations established specifically for women who have been circumcised in the USA, but the following organizations have been friendly to the author. Please go to Circumcision Information and Resource Pages at www.cirp.org for clickable links to web sites for most of these wonderful resources or enter the organization's name into your web browser's search engine.

GENERAL EDUCATION/INFORMATION
Accord Alliance
Circumcision Information Australia
Circumcision Information Resource Center, Montreal, Canada
Circumcision Information and Resource Pages (www.cirp.org)
Circumcision Resource Center, Boston, Massachusetts
The History of Circumcision
National Organization of Circumcision Information Resource Centers (NOCIRC), San Anselmo, California, USA
The National Sexuality Resource Center (NSRC), San Francisco State University
www.phimose-info.de (site in German language)
www.waterbirth.org

PROFESSIONALS
Attorneys for the Rights of the Child
Doctors Opposing Circumcision, DoctorsOpposingCircumcision.org
Nurses for the Rights of the Child
Physicians for Human Rights

PARENTS
Circumcision: A Collection of Information Resources for Expectant Fathers by Robin Verner
Kahal, the Israeli Parents' group
Mothers Against Circumcision

PATIENT'S RIGHTS
Informed Consent (www.informedconsent.org)
The Intersex Society of North America (ISNA)

FOR MEN
Circumcision Issues and Foreskin Restoration Techniques by Gary Burlingame
The Men's Media Network
Menstuff. The National Men's Resource
The National Coalition of Free Men (NCFM)
National Organization to Halt the Abuse and Routine Mutilation of Males (NOHARMM)
National Organization of Restoring Men (NORM)
National Organization of Restoring Men - Southern California chapter: NORM-SC
NORM-UK (Great Britain)

FOR WOMEN
San Diego Birth Network, http://www.birthresourcenetwork.org/
Christiane Northrup, M.D. www.drnorthrup.com

ACTIVISM
The Ashley Montagu Resolution
Association contre la Mutilation des Enfants (AME) in Boulogne, France. (French and English pages)

www.CourtChallenge.com An application to the Court Challenges Program in Canada for funding to mount a legal challenge to protect children.
www.Intact.CA
International Coalition for Genital Integrity (ICGI)
Mutilation of Males (NOHARMM)
www.MGMbill.org. Promoting a bill to end male genital mutilation in the USA
med-fraud.org
National Organization to Halt the Abuse and Routine
Students for Genital Integrity
Stop Mutilating Children (UK)

RELIGIONS
Catholics Against Circumcision
Gonen Al Hayeled (Protect the Child) (site in Hebrew language)
The Israeli Association Against Genital Mutilation
Jews Against Circumcision

INFORMATION & COMMENTARY
Circumcizia.org (site in Romanian language)
Circumstitions.com (Hugh Young)
Historical Medical Quotes on Circumcision
Negative Aspects of Routine Infant Circumcision by Wayne Hampton
Porn Flakes: Kellogg, Graham and the Crusade for Moral Fiber by Carrie McLaren (the history of circumcision in America)
The Ridged Band: Specialized Sexual Tissue. Research into the anatomy and function of the intact penis. Informational site created by sex researchers
Robert Riley's Circumcision Information Center
SexAsNatureIntendedIt.com by Kristen and Jeffrey O'Hara
SexuallyMutilatedChild.org by John A. Erickson. Powerful, graphic, moving

LEGAL ASSISTANCE
David Llewellyn, Atlanta, Georgia
John Geishinger, attorney for Doctors Opposing Circumcision (DOC), Seattle, Washington

Steven Svoboda, Attorneys for the Rights of the Child (ARC), Berkeley, California

ENTERTAINMENT *(See also a vast array of videos at youtube.com)*
Cut/Uncut: A Play Against Circumcision intactamerica.rg/2008/12/ cut-uncut-a-play-against-circumcision/Youtube.com and videos.google. com host many videos about circumcision
Global Women Intact, Amma's one-woman plays
It's a Boy! A Circus Opera www.noharmm.org/circumopera.htm and www.cdbaby.com/cd/romanovsky2

FOR REASONS OF LEGALITY

Neither the author of this book nor the publisher advocates the use of any particular form of health care but believes that the information presented herein should be available to every person concerned with improving his or her health or that of a child.

Although the author has attempted to give an accurate and complete presentation of the topics discussed and to ensure accuracy and completeness of any information that originates from any source other than her own, she and the publisher assume no responsibility for errors, inaccuracies, omissions, or any inconsistency herein.

This book takes aim at unintentional abuse, not persons. It does not intend to harm any individual, ethic group, religious organization or professional corporation. This book is not intended to replace the advice and treatment of a competent, compassionate, wise physician who specializes in helping patients achieve and maintain radiant health.

Any use of the information set forth herein is entirely at the reader's discretion. The author and publisher are not responsible for any adverse effects or consequences resulting from the use of any of the information or procedures described in this book. Readers should use their own judgment or consult a holistic medical expert or their personal physician(s) for specific applications.